Christian Hymnways

A collection of hymns and worship
materials for the Church School, for
Youth, and other kindred groups.

The Christian Education Press

PHILADELPHIA   ST. LOUIS

Foreword

The preparation of "Christian Hymnways" has been a labor of love, and it is now affectionately dedicated to the host of men and women who are seeking the best ways and means of cultivating the spirit and habit of sincere and intelligent Christian worship. The book is launched with the earnest prayer that it may enrich the worship services in Church Schools, Young People's Societies and kindred organizations.

The Editorial Committee has carefully chosen musical gems, old and new, from the treasury of Christian hymnody. This compilation of hymns and worship material forms a volume, limited in scope and price, that we believe to be adapted to the nature and nurture both of growing youth and adults, a worthy means for the expression of their praise and prayer.

In the classification of hymns, the main seasons of the Church year were followed, with due recognition of the observance of special days. Copious indices of hymns and tunes are provided. Care was taken to secure accuracy of data. The several stanzas of each hymn are put in their proper place between the staves, and their number is kept within the time available for hymns in the worship program. In the choice of the score, high musical quality and vocal range were determining factors.

Special care was given to the liturgical material, the aim being to provide helps for actual use, and also for the building of original worship services. Leaders will find guidance in a section dealing with the principles of worship, and in a few typical services which we especially commend for their study.

"Christian Hymnways" is the result of the cooperation of many hearts and minds, sharing earnestly in the desire to provide a suitable medium to the various organizations of the Church for the expression and cultivation of their religious experience and to prepare them for fruitful participation in the worship of the sanctuary. Gratefully we express our obligation to all who have so generously given of their time and talent to make this book a reality.

THEO. F. HERMAN, Chairman,
C. A. HAUSER
A. R. KEPPEL
PAUL S. LEINBACH
H. A. PFLUG
F. C. RUEGGEBERG

Acknowledgment

For the use of all copyrighted hymns, readings and music included in this hymnal, permission has been secured from the author or from his authorized publisher.

Every effort has been made to trace the ownership of all copyright material. Should any infringement have been unconsciously made, the Publishers desire hereby to express their regrets. They will be glad on notification to make proper acknowledgment in future editions of this book.

Table of Contents

GENERAL INDEX

Hymns listed alphabetically according to first lines
(Asterisks indicate hymns especially suitable for Juniors)

GENERAL INDEX

Topical Index

TOPICAL INDEX

Index of Tunes

Christian Hymnways

When Morning Gilds the Skies

Anonymous (German)
Tr. by Edward Caswall

LAUDES DOMINI

Joseph Barnby

1. When morn-ing gilds the skies, My heart a-wak-ing cries,
2. The night be-comes as day, When from the heart we say,
3. Ye na-tions of man-kind, In this your con-cord find,
4. Be this, while life is mine, My can-ti-cle di-vine,

May Je-sus Christ be praised! A-like at work and prayer,
May Je-sus Christ be praised! The powers of dark-ness fear,
May Je-sus Christ be praised! Let all the earth a-round
May Je-sus Christ be praised! Be this th' e-ter-nal song,

To Je-sus I re-pair; May Je-sus Christ be praised!
When this sweet chant they hear, May Je-sus Christ be praised!
Ring joy-ous with the sound, May Je-sus Christ be praised!
Through all the a-ges long, May Je-sus Christ be praised! A-MEN.

2

Holy, Holy, Holy

Reginald Heber

NICÆA

John B. Dykes

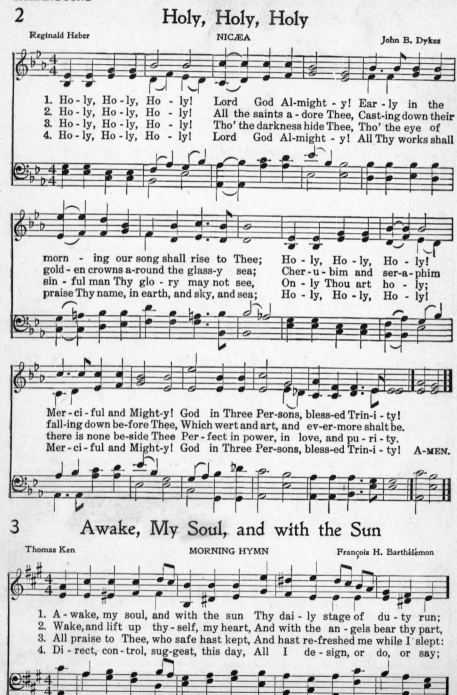

1. Ho - ly, Ho - ly, Ho - ly! Lord God Al-might - y! Ear - ly in the
2. Ho - ly, Ho - ly, Ho - ly! All the saints a - dore Thee, Cast-ing down their
3. Ho - ly, Ho - ly, Ho - ly! Tho' the darkness hide Thee, Tho' the eye of
4. Ho - ly, Ho - ly, Ho - ly! Lord God Al-might - y! All Thy works shall

morn - ing our song shall rise to Thee; Ho - ly, Ho - ly, Ho - ly!
gold - en crowns a-round the glass-y sea; Cher-u-bim and ser-a-phim
sin - ful man Thy glo - ry may not see, On - ly Thou art ho - ly;
praise Thy name, in earth, and sky, and sea; Ho - ly, Ho - ly, Ho - ly!

Mer - ci - ful and Might-y! God in Three Per-sons, bless-ed Trin-i - ty!
fall-ing down be-fore Thee, Which wert and art, and ev-er-more shalt be.
there is none be-side Thee Per - fect in power, in love, and pu - ri - ty.
Mer - ci - ful and Might-y! God in Three Per-sons, bless-ed Trin-i - ty! A-MEN.

3

Awake, My Soul, and with the Sun

Thomas Ken

MORNING HYMN

François H. Barthélemon

1. A - wake, my soul, and with the sun Thy dai - ly stage of du - ty run;
2. Wake, and lift up thy - self, my heart, And with the an - gels bear thy part,
3. All praise to Thee, who safe hast kept, And hast re-freshed me while I slept:
4. Di - rect, con - trol, sug-gest, this day, All I de - sign, or do, or say;

Awake, My Soul, and with the Sun

Shake off dull sloth, and joy - ful rise To pay thy morn-ing sac-ri - fice.
Who all night long un-wear-ied sing High praise to the E - ter-nal King.
Grant, Lord, that I from death shall wake, I may of end-less life par-take.
That all my powers, with all their might, In Thy sole glo - ry may u - nite. A-MEN.

Still, Still with Thee

4

Harriet Beecher Stowe   SANDRINGHAM   Joseph Barnby

1. Still, still with Thee, when pur - ple morn-ing break-eth, When the bird
2. A - lone with Thee, a - mid the mys - tic shad - ows, The sol-emn
3. When sinks the soul, sub - dued by toil, to slum - ber, Its clos-ing
4. So shall it be at last, in that bright morn-ing When the soul

wak - eth, and the shad-ows flee, Fair - er than morn-ing, love - lier than the
hush of na - ture new - ly born; A - lone with Thee in breath-less ad - o-
eyes look up to Thee in prayer; Sweet the re - pose be-neath Thy wings o'er-
wak - eth, and the shad-ows flee; Oh, in that hour, fair - er than day-light

day - light, Dawns the sweet con-scious-ness, I am with Thee.
ra - tion, In the calm dew and fresh-ness of the morn.
shad - ing, But sweet-er still to wake and find Thee there.
dawn-ing, Shall rise the glo-rious thought—I am with Thee. A - MEN.

5   O God, Thy World Is Sweet with Prayer

Lucy Larcom   CANONBURY   Robert Schumann

1. O God, Thy world is sweet with prayer; The breath of Christ is in the air;
2. Thou art our Morn-ing and our Sun, Our work is glad, in Thee be-gun,
3. O God, with-in us and a-bove, Close to us in the Christ we love,

We rise on Thy free Spir-it's wings, And ev-ery thought within us sings.
Our foot-worn path is fresh with dew, For Thou cre-at-est all things new.
Through Him, our on-ly guide and way, May heavenly life be ours to-day! A-MEN.

6   Come, O Lord, Like Morning Sunlight

Milton S. Littlefield   LUCERNE   T. A. Willis

1. Come, O Lord, like morn-ing sun-light, Mak-ing all life new and free;
2. Come, O Lord, like o-cean flood-tides, Flow-ing in-land from the sea;
3. Come, O Lord, like moun-tain breez-es, Freshening life in vale and lea;
4. Come, O Lord, like eve-ning twi-light, Bring-ing peace on land and sea;

For the dai-ly task and chal-lenge May we rise re-newed in Thee.
As the wa-ters fill the shal-lows, May our souls be filled with Thee.
In the heat and stress of du-ty May our souls find strength in Thee.
At the ra-diant close of la-bor May our souls find rest in Thee. A-MEN.

Words Copyright by Milton S. Littlefield.

The Shadows of the Evening Hours

Adelaide A. Procter
DOLE
William Lester

1. The shad-ows of the eve-ning hours Fall from the dark-ening sky;
2. The sor-rows of Thy serv-ants, Lord, O do not Thou de-spise,
3. Slow-ly the rays of day-light fade: So fade with-in our heart
4. Let peace, O Lord, Thy peace, O God, Up-on our souls de-scend;

Up-on the fra-grance of the flowers The dews of eve-ning lie.
But let the in-cense of our prayers Be-fore Thy mer-cy rise.
The hopes in earth-ly love and joy, That one by one de-part.
From mid-night fears, and per-ils, Thou Our trem-bling hearts de-fend.

Be-fore Thy throne, O God of heaven, We kneel at close of day;
The bright-ness of the com-ing night Up-on the dark-ness rolls;
Slow-ly the bright stars, one by one, With-in the heav-ens shine:
Give us a res-pite from our toil; Calm and sub-due our woes;

Look on Thy chil-dren from on high, And hear us while we pray.
With hopes of fu-ture glo-ry chase The shad-ows from our souls.
Give us, O Lord, fresh hopes in heaven, And trust in things di-vine.
Through the long day we la-bor, Lord, O give us now re-pose. A-MEN.

Day Is Dying in the West

Mary A. Lathbury   CHAUTAUQUA   William F. Sherwin

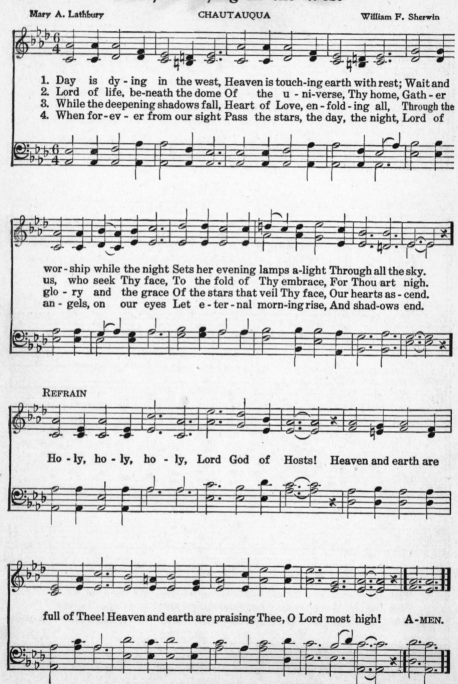

1. Day is dy-ing in the west, Heaven is touch-ing earth with rest; Wait and
2. Lord of life, be-neath the dome Of the u-ni-verse, Thy home, Gath-er
3. While the deepening shadows fall, Heart of Love, en-fold-ing all, Through the
4. When for-ev-er from our sight Pass the stars, the day, the night, Lord of

wor-ship while the night Sets her evening lamps a-light Through all the sky.
us, who seek Thy face, To the fold of Thy embrace, For Thou art nigh.
glo-ry and the grace Of the stars that veil Thy face, Our hearts as-cend.
an-gels, on our eyes Let e-ter-nal morn-ing rise, And shad-ows end.

REFRAIN

Ho-ly, ho-ly, ho-ly, Lord God of Hosts! Heaven and earth are

full of Thee! Heaven and earth are praising Thee, O Lord most high! A-MEN.

God That Madest Earth and Heaven

Reginald Heber
William Mercer, stanza 2
Richard Whately, stanza 3

AR HYD Y NOS

Welsh traditional melody
Harmonized by L. O. Emerson

1. God, that mad-est earth and heav-en, Dark-ness and light;
2. And when morn a-gain shall call us To run life's way;
3. Guard us wak-ing, guard us sleep-ing, And when we die,

Who the day for toil hast giv-en, For rest the night;
May we still, what-e'er be-fall us, Thy will o-bey.
May we in Thy might-y keep-ing All peace-ful lie;

May Thine an-gel guards de-fend us, Slum-ber sweet Thy mer-cy send us;
From the power of e-vil hide us, In the nar-row path-way guide us.
When the last dread call shall wake us, Do not Thou, our God, for-sake us,

Ho-ly dreams and hopes at-tend us, This live-long night.
Nor Thy smile be e'er de-nied us The live-long day.
But to reign in glo-ry take us With Thee on high. A-MEN.

10 Abide with Me

Henry F. Lyte · EVENTIDE · William H. Monk

1. A - bide with me: fast falls the e - ven - tide; The dark - ness
2. Swift to its close ebbs out life's lit - tle day; Earth's joys grow
3. I need Thy pres - ence ev - er - y pass - ing hour: What but Thy
4. Hold Thou Thy cross be - fore my clos - ing eyes; Shine through the

deep - ens; Lord, with me a - bide: When oth - er help - ers fail, and
dim, its glo - ries pass a - way; Change and de - cay in all a -
grace can foil the tempter's power? Who like Thy - self my guide and
gloom, and point me to the skies: Heaven's morning breaks, and earth's vain

com - forts flee, Help of the help - less, O a - bide with me!
round I see; O Thou, who chang - est not, a - bide with me!
stay can be? Through cloud and sunshine, O a - bide with me!
shad - ows flee: In life, in death, O Lord, a - bide with me! A-MEN.

11 Now the Day Is Over

Sabine Baring-Gould · MERRIAL · Joseph Barnby

1. Now the day is o - ver, Night is draw - ing nigh;
2. Je - sus, give the wea - ry Calm and sweet re - pose;
3. Com - fort ev - er - y suf - ferer Watch - ing late in pain;
4. Through the long night-watch - es May Thine an - gels spread
5. When the morn - ing wak - ens, Then may I a - rise

Now the Day Is Over

At Even, When the Sun Was Set 12

ANGELUS

Henry Twells

Georg Joseph
"Heilige Seelenlust"

13 Peacefully Round Us the Shadows are Falling

Ambrose N. Blatchford   CURFEW   Frederick C. Maker

1. Peace-ful-ly round us the shad-ows are fall - ing, Glad be our
2. Hushed are the sheep-bells a - far on the moor - land, O'er the still
3. Soft - ly may wea-ry ones rest from their du - ty, Bright be the
4. Lord of the night, let Thine an-gels de - fend us; Sun-shine and

prais-es and trust-ful our prayer: Hear us, O Lord, on Thy prov-i-dence
mead-ows the night breez-es sweep, Faint fall the foot-steps in cit-y and
dreams of the troub-led and worn, While through the shade beam the stars in their
gloom are a - like un-to Thee: Lord of the day, let Thy Spir-it at-

call - ing, Light-en our dark-ness, and ban-ish our care.
ham - let, Safe-ly the chil-dren are fold-ed in sleep.
beau - ty, Watch-ing the world till the break-ing of morn.
tend us, Bless us and keep us wher-ev-er we be. A - MEN.

14 Sun of My Soul

HURSLEY

John Keble

Peter Ritter
Arr. by W. H. Mock

1. Son of my soul! Thou Sav-iour dear, It is not night if Thou be near;
2. When the soft dews of kind-ly sleep My wea-ry eye-lids gen-tly steep,
3. A - bide with me from morn till eve, For with-out Thee I can-not live;
4. Come near and bless us when we wake, Ere through the world our way we take;

Sun of My Soul

O may no earth-born cloud a - rise To hide Thee from Thy serv-ant's eyes.
Be my last thought, how sweet to rest For-ev - er on my Sav-iour's breast.
A - bide with me when night is nigh, For with-out Thee I dare not die.
Till, in the o - cean of Thy love, We lose our - selves in heaven a-bove. A-MEN.

Saviour, Again to Thy Dear Name   15

ELLERS

John Ellerton

Edward J. Hopkins

1. Sav - iour, a - gain to Thy dear name we raise With one ac-
2. Grant us Thy peace up - on our home-ward way; With Thee be-
3. Grant us Thy peace, Lord, through the com-ing night, Turn Thou for
4. Grant us Thy peace through-out our earth - ly life, Our balm in

cord our part - ing hymn of praise; We stand to bless Thee ere our
gan, with Thee shall end the day; Guard Thou the lips from sin, the
us its dark-ness in - to light; From harm and dan - ger keep Thy
sor - row, and our stay in strife; Then, when Thy voice shall bid our

wor - ship cease; Then, low - ly kneel - ing, wait Thy word of peace.
hearts from shame, That in this house have called up - on Thy name.
chil - dren free, For dark and light are both a - like to Thee.
con - flict cease, Call us, O Lord, to Thine e - ter - nal peace. A-MEN.

16 The Lord Bless You and Keep You

Numbers 6: 24-26   BENEDICTION   Peter C. Lutkin

The Lord bless you and keep you, The Lord lift His coun-te-nance up-

on you, and give you peace, and give you peace; The Lord

and give you peace,..........and give you peace;..........The Lord

Lord make His face and be gra - - - cious un-to

make His face to shine up-on you. The Lord be gra-cious,

you, be gra-cious,

The Lord be gra-cious, The Lord be gra-cious, gra-cious un-to you. A - MEN.

17 Day Is Done, Gone the Sun

Anonymous   TAPS

Day is done, gone the sun, from the lake, from the hills, from the

sky, Safe-ly rest, all is well, God is nigh.

We Praise Thee, O God, Our Lord

HANOVER

Ambrose M. Schmidt

William Croft

1. We praise Thee, O God, our Lord and our King!
2. We praise Thee, O God, for Thy guid - ing hand,
3. We praise Thee, O God, for years of in - crease,
4. We pray Thee, O Christ, our Help - er and Friend!

Ac - cept Thou the praise we grate - ful - ly bring;
In lead - ing Thy Church to free - dom's fair land;
For faith un - as - sailed, pros - per - i - ty, peace;
From er - ror and strife, our Zi - on de - fend!

Thanks - giv - ing and wor - ship we of - fer to Thee,
Through sore per - se - cu - tion our fa - thers here came,
U - nit - ed we of - fer our an - them of praise
Breathe on us, we pray Thee, O Spir - it of Love,

Thou Rul - er of na - tions, in whom we are free!
Where free and un - fet - tered they wor-shipped Thy name.
To Thee our Sup - port - er, our An - cient of Days.
And fit us for un - ion with Thy Church a - bove. A - MEN.

19 Joyful, Joyful, We Adore Thee

Henry van Dyke   HYMN TO JOY   Ludwig van Beethoven

1. Joy - ful, joy - ful, we a - dore Thee, God of glo - ry, Lord of love;
2. All Thy works with joy sur-round Thee, Earth and heaven re-flect Thy rays,
3. Thou art giv - ing and for - giv - ing, Ev - er bless-ing, ev - er blest,
4. Mor-tals join the might - y cho - rus, Which the morn-ing stars be - gan;

Hearts un - fold like flowers be - fore Thee, Ope-ning to the sun a - bove.
Stars and an - gels sing a - round Thee, Cen - ter of un - bro - ken praise:
Well-spring of the joy of liv - ing, O - cean-depth of hap - py rest!
Fa - ther-love is reign-ing o'er us, Broth-er-love binds man to man.

Melt the clouds of sin and sad - ness; Drive the dark of doubt a - way;
Field and for - est, vale and moun-tain, Bloom-ing mead-ow, flash - ing sea,
Thou our Fa - ther, Christ our Broth-er, — All who live in love are Thine:
Ev - er sing - ing march we on - ward, Vic - tors in the midst of strife;

Giv - er of im - mor - tal glad-ness, Fill us with the light of day!
Chanting bird and flow - ing foun-tain, Call us to re - joice in Thee.
Teach us how to love each oth - er, Lift us to the Joy Di-vine.
Joy - ful mu - sic lifts us sun-ward In the tri-umph song of life. A-MEN.

Praise the Lord, Ye Heavens, Adore Him   20

Stanzas 1, 2, Anonymous
Stanza 3, Edward Osler

FABEN

John H. Willcox

1. Praise the Lord, ye heavens, a-dore Him, Praise Him, an-gels, in the height;
2. Praise the Lord, for He is glo-rious, Nev - er shall His prom-ise fail;
3. Wor - ship, hon - or, glo - ry, bless-ing, Lord, we of - fer un - to Thee;

Sun and moon, re - joice be - fore Him; Praise Him, all ye stars of light.
God hath made His saints vic - to - rious, Sin and death shall not pre-vail.
Young and old, Thy praise ex-press - ing, In glad hom - age bend the knee.

Praise the Lord, for He hath spo - ken; Worlds His might-y voice o - beyed;
Praise the God of our sal - va - tion; Hosts on high, His power pro-claim;
All   the saints in heaven a - dore Thee, We would bow be - fore Thy throne;

Laws which nev-er shall be bro - ken, For their guidance He hath made.
Heaven and earth and all cre - a - tion, Laud and mag-ni - fy His name.
As Thine an-gels serve be-fore Thee, So on earth Thy will be done. A - MEN.

21 Come, Thou Almighty King

Author unknown

ITALIAN HYMN

Felice de Giardini

1. Come, Thou Al - might - y King, Help us Thy name to sing,
2. Come, Thou In - car - nate Word, Gird on Thy might - y sword,
3. Come, Ho - ly Com - fort - er, Thy sa - cred wit - ness bear
4. To Thee, great One in Three, E - ter - nal prais - es be

Help us to praise: Fa - ther, all glo - ri - ous, O'er all vic -
Our prayer at - tend: Come, and Thy peo - ple bless, And give Thy
In this glad hour: Thou who al - might - y art, Now rule in
Hence, ev - er - more! His sov - ereign maj - es - ty May we in

to - ri - ous, Come, and reign o - ver us, An - cient of Days.
Word suc-cess: Spir - it of ho - li - ness, On us de - scend.
ev - ery heart, And ne'er from us de-part, Spir - it of power.
glo - ry see, And to e - ter - ni - ty Love and a - dore! A - MEN.

22 Lord of All Being

Oliver Wendell Holmes

LOUVAN

Virgil C. Taylor

1. Lord of all be - ing, throned a-far, Thy glo - ry flames from sun and star;
2. Sun of our life, Thy quickening ray Sheds on our path the glow of day;
3. Lord of all life, be - low, a - bove, Whose light is truth, whose warmth is love;
4. Grant us Thy truth to make us free, And kin - dling hearts that burn for Thee,

Lord of All Being

Cen - ter and soul of ev - ery sphere, Yet to each lov-ing heart how near!
Star of our hope, Thy softened light Cheers the long watches of the night.
Be - fore Thy ev - er - blaz-ing throne We ask no lus - ter of our own.
Till all Thy liv - ing al - tars claim One ho - ly light, one heavenly flame. A-MEN.

O Worship the King   23

Robert Grant   LYONS   J. Michael Haydn

1. O wor-ship the King, all - glo-rious a - bove, O grate-ful - ly
2. O tell of His might, O sing of His grace, Whose robe is the
3. Thy boun - ti - ful care what tongue can re - cite? It breathes in the
4. Frail chil - dren of dust, and fee - ble as frail, In Thee do we

sing His power and His love; Our Shield and De-fend - er, the An - cient of
light, whose can-o - py space. His char - iots of wrath the deep thun-der-clouds
air, it shines in the light, It streams from the hills, it de-scends to the
trust, nor find Thee to fail; Thy mer - cies how ten-der! how firm to the

Days, Pa - vil - ioned in splen-dor, and gird - ed with praise.
form, And dark is His path on the wings of the storm.
plain, And sweet-ly dis - tills in the dew and the rain.
end! Our Mak - er, De - fend - er, Re - deem - er and Friend. A - MEN.

24 Rejoice, Ye Pure in Heart

Edward H. Plumptre   MARION   Arthur M. Messiter

1. Re - joice, ye pure in heart, Re - joice, give thanks, and sing:
2. With all the an - gel choirs, With all the saints on earth,
3. Still lift your stand - ard high, Still march in firm ar - ray;
4. Yes, on through life's long path, Still chant - ing as ye go;
5. Then on, ye pure in heart, Re - joice, give thanks, and sing;

Your fes - tal ban - ner wave on high, The cross of Christ your King.
Pour out the strains of joy and bliss, True rap - ture, no - blest mirth!
As war - riors through the dark - ness toil Till dawns the gold - en day.
From youth to age, by night and day, In glad - ness and in woe.
Your fes - tal ban - ner wave on high, The cross of Christ your King.

REFRAIN

Re - joice, re - joice, Re - joice, give thanks, and sing! A - MEN

Re-joice, re-joice,

25 Let Us with a Gladsome Mind

INNOCENTS

John Milton   The Parish Choir

1. Let us with a glad - some mind Praise the Lord, for He is kind:
2. He with all com-mand-ing might, Filled the new-made world with light;
3. All things liv - ing He doth feed; His full hand sup - plies their need:
4. Let us, then, His praise sing forth, His high ma - jes - ty and worth:

Let Us with a Gladsome Mind

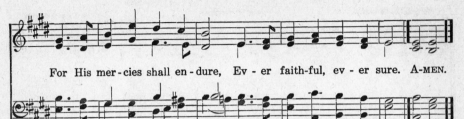

For His mer-cies shall en-dure, Ev - er faith-ful, ev - er sure. A-MEN.

We Praise Thee, O God, Our Redeemer 26

KREMSER

Julia Bulkley Cady

Netherlands Folksong from
The Collection by Andrianus Valerius

1. We praise Thee, O God, our Re-deem-er, Cre - a - tor, In grate-ful de-
2. We wor - ship Thee, God of our fa-thers, we bless Thee; Through life's storm and
3. With voic - es u - nit - ed our prais-es we of - fer, To Thee, great Je-

vo - tion our trib-ute we bring. We lay it be-fore Thee, we kneel and a-
tempest our Guide hast Thou been. When per-ils o'er-take us, es - cape Thou wilt
ho - vah, glad an-thems we raise. Thy strong arm will guide us, our God is be-

dore Thee, We bless Thy ho - ly name, glad prais-es we sing.
make us, And with Thy help, O Lord, our bat - tles we win.
side us, To Thee, our great Re-deem-er, for - ev - er be praise. A - MEN.

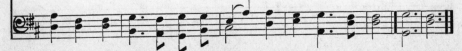

27 O Day of Rest and Gladness

Christopher Wordsworth · MENDEBRAS · Arr. by Lowell Mason

1. O day of rest and glad-ness, O day of joy and light,
2. On thee, at the cre - a - tion, The light first had its birth;
3. To - day on wea-ry na-tions The heaven-ly man-na falls:
4. New grac - es ev - er gain-ing From this our day of rest,

O balm of care and sad-ness, Most beau - ti - ful, most bright;
On thee, for our sal - va - tion, Christ rose from depths of earth;
To ho - ly con - vo - ca - tions The sil - ver trump-et calls,
We reach the rest re - main-ing To spir - its of the blest.

On thee, the high and low - ly, Through a - ges joined in tune,
On thee, our Lord, vic - to - rious, The Spir - it sent from heaven;
Where gos - pel light is glow-ing With pure and ra - diant beams,
To Ho - ly Ghost be prais-es, To Fa - ther, and to Son;

Sing Ho - ly, Ho - ly, Ho - ly, To the great God Tri - une.
And thus on thee, most glo-rious, A tri - ple light was given.
And liv - ing wa - ter flow-ing With soul - re - fresh-ing streams.
The Church her voice up - rais - es To Thee, blest Three in One. A-MEN.

Ancient of Days

William C. Doane   ANCIENT OF DAYS   J. Albert Jeffery

1. An - cient of Days, who sit - test throned in glo - ry,
2. O Ho - ly Fa - ther, who hast led Thy chil - dren,
3. O Ho - ly Je - sus, Prince of Peace and Sav - iour,
4. O Ho - ly Ghost, the Lord and the Life - giv - er,
5. O Tri - une God, with heart and voice a - dor - ing,

To Thee all knees are bent, all voic - es pray;
In all the a - ges, with the fire and cloud,
To Thee we owe the peace that still pre - vails,
Thine is the quick - ening power that gives in - crease;
Praise we the good - ness that doth crown our days;

Thy love hast blest the wide world's won - drous sto - ry
Through seas dry - shod, through wea - ry wastes be - wil - dering;
Still - ing the rude wills of men's wild be - hav - ior,
From Thee have flowed, as from a pleas - ant riv - er,
Pray we that Thou wilt hear us, still im - plor - ing

With light and life since E - den's dawn - ing day.
To Thee, in rev - erent love, our hearts are bowed.
And calm - ing pas - sion's fierce and storm - y gales.
Our plen - ty, wealth, pros - per - i - ty and peace.
Thy love and fa - vor, kept to us al - ways. A - MEN.

All Hail the Power

Edward Perronet   CORONATION   Oliver Holden

1. All hail the power of Je - sus' name! Let an - gels pros-trate fall;
2. Ye cho - sen seed of Is - rael's race, Ye ran-somed from the fall,
3. Let ev - ery kin - dred, ev - ery tribe, On this ter - res - trial ball,
4. O that with yon - der sa - cred throng We at His feet may fall!

Bring forth the roy - al di - a - dem, And crown Him Lord of all;
Hail Him who saves you by His grace, And crown Him Lord of all;
To Him all maj - es - ty as - cribe, And crown Him Lord of all;
We'll join the ev - er - last - ing song, And crown Him Lord of all;

Bring forth the roy - al di - a - dem, And crown Him Lord of all!
Hail Him who saves you by His grace, And crown Him Lord of all!
To Him all maj - es - ty as - cribe, And crown Him Lord of all!
We'll join the ev - er - last - ing song, And crown Him Lord of all! A-MEN.

(*Second Tune*)   MILES LANE   William Shrubsole

1. All hail the power of Je-sus' name! Let angels prostrate fall; Bring forth the roy-al

di - a - dem, And crown Him, crown Him, crown Him, Crown Him Lord of all! A-MEN.

Crown Him with Many Crowns

Matthew Bridges   DIADEMATA   George J. Elvey

1. Crown Him with man - y crowns, The Lamb up - on His throne;
2. Crown Him the Lord of love: Be - hold His hands and side,
3. Crown Him the Lord of peace; Whose power a scep - ter sways
4. Crown Him the Lord of years, The Po - ten - tate of time;

Hark! how the heaven-ly an-them drowns All mu - sic but its own:
Rich wounds, yet vis - i - ble a - bove, In beau - ty glo - ri - fied:
From pole to pole, that wars may cease, Ab - sorbed in prayer and praise:
Cre - a - tor of the roll - ing spheres, In - ef - fa - bly sub - lime:

A - wake, my soul, and sing Of Him who died for thee, And
No an - gel in the sky Can ful - ly bear that sight, But
His reign shall know no end; And round His pierc - ed feet Fair
All hail, Re - deem - er, hail! For Thou hast died for me: Thy

hail Him as thy match-less King Through all e - ter - ni - ty.
down-ward bends his burn-ing eye At mys - ter - ies so bright.
flowers of Par - a - dise ex - tend Their fra-grance ev - er sweet.
praise shall nev - er, nev - er fail Through-out e - ter - ni - ty. A - MEN.

31 Fairest Lord Jesus

CRUSADERS' HYMN

German, 17th century

Silesian Folk song
Arr. by Richard S. Willis

1. Fair - est Lord Je - sus! Rul - er of all na - ture!
2. Fair are the mead - ows, Fair - er still the wood - lands,
3. Fair is the sun - shine, Fair - er still the moon - light,

O Thou of God and man the Son! Thee will I cher - ish,
Robed in the bloom - ing garb of spring: Je - sus is fair - er,
And all the twin - kling star - ry host; Je - sus shines bright - er,

Thee will I hon - or, Thou, my soul's glo - ry, joy, and crown!
Je - sus is pur - er, Who makes the woe - ful heart to sing.
Je - sus shines pur - er Than all the an - gels heaven can boast! A-MEN.

32 Yes, God Is Good; in Earth and Sky

John H. Gurney
From a poem by Elizabeth L. Follen

TRURO

T. Williams' "Psalmodia Evangelica"

1. Yes, God is good; in earth and sky, From o - cean depths and spreading wood,
2. The sun that keeps his trackless way And down-ward pours his gold - en flood,
3. The mer - ry birds pro-long the strain, Their song with ev - ery spring re-newed;
4. Yes, God is good, all na - ture says, By God's own hand with speech en - dued;

Yes, God Is Good; in Earth and Sky

Ten thousand voic-es seem to cry,"God made us all, and God is good."
Night's sparkling hosts, all seem to say, In ac-cents clear, that God is good.
And balm-y air, and fall-ing rain, Each soft-ly whis-pers,"God is good."
And man, in loud-er notes of praise, Should sing for joy that God is good. AMEN.

For the Beauty of the Earth   33

Folliott S. Pierpoint   DIX   Conrad Kocher

1. For the beau-ty of the earth, For the glo-ry of the skies,
2. For the won-der of each hour, Of the day and of the night,
3. For the joy of hu-man love, Broth-er, sis-ter, par-ent, child,
4. For Thy church that ev-er-more Lift-eth ho-ly hands a-bove,

For the love which from our birth O-ver and a-round us lies,
Hill and vale, and tree and flower, Sun and moon, and stars of light,
Friends on earth, and friends a-bove, For all gen-tle thoughts and mild,
Of-fering up on ev-ery shore Her pure sac-ri-fice of love,

REFRAIN

Lord of all, to Thee we raise This our hymn of grate-ful praise. A-MEN.

34 God of the Earth, the Sky, the Sea

PATER OMNIUM. With Refrain

Samuel Longfellow

Henry J. E. Holmes

1. God of the earth, the sky, the sea! Mak-er of all a - bove, be-low!
2. Thy love is in the sunshine's glow, Thy life is in the quick-ening air;
3. We feel Thy calm at evening's hour, Thy grandeur in the march of night;
4. But high-er far, and far more clear, Thee in man's spir-it we be - hold,

Cre - a - tion lives and moves in Thee, Thy pres-ent life through all doth flow.
When lightnings flash and storm-winds blow, There is Thy power; Thy law is there.
And, when Thy morn-ing breaks in power, We hear Thy word, "Let there be light."
Thine im-age and Thy-self are there,—Th' in-dwell-ing God, proclaimed of old.

REFRAIN

We give Thee thanks, Thy name we sing, Al-might-y Fa-ther, heaven-ly King. A-MEN.

35 O Maker of the Sea and Sky

SANTA TRINITA

Henry Burton

E. Pieraccini

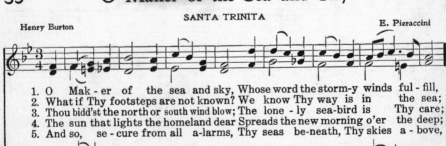

1. O Mak-er of the sea and sky, Whose word the storm-y winds ful-fill,
2. What if Thy footsteps are not known? We know Thy way is in the sea;
3. Thou bidd'st the north or south wind blow; The lone - ly sea-bird is Thy care;
4. The sun that lights the homeland dear Spreads the new morning o'er the deep;
5. And so, se-cure from all a-larms, Thy seas be-neath, Thy skies a - bove,

O Maker of the Sea and Sky

On the wide o - cean Thou art nigh, Bidding these hearts of ours be still.
We trace the shad-ow of Thy throne, Constant a - mid in - con - stan-cy.
And in the clouds which come and go, We see Thy char-iots ev - ery-where.
And in the dark Thy stars ap-pear, Keeping their watches while we sleep.
Clasped in the ev - er - last-ing arms, We rest in Thine un-slum-bering love. A-MEN.

The Heavens Declare Thy Glory   36

Thomas R. Birks   CHENIES   Timothy R. Matthews

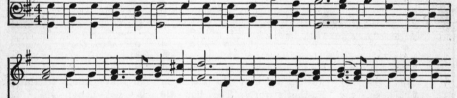

1. The heavens declare Thy glory, The firmament Thy power; Day un - to day the
2. The sun with roy - al splen-dor Goes forth to chant Thy praise, And moonbeams soft and
3. All heaven on high re - joic - es To do its Mak-er's will; The stars with sol-emn

sto - ry Re-peats from hour to hour; Night un-to night re - ply - ing, Proclaims in
ten-der Their gentler anthem raise: O'er ev-ery tribe and na - tion The mu - sic
voic-es Re-sound Thy prais-es still: So let my whole be - hav-ior, Thoughts,words,and

ev - ery land, O Lord, with voice un-dy - ing, The won-ders of Thy hand.
strange is poured; The song of all cre - a - tion To Thee, cre-a-tion's Lord.
ac - tions be, O Lord, my Strength, my Saviour, One ceaseless song to Thee. A-MEN.

This Is My Father's World

TERRA BEATA

Maltbie D. Babcock

Traditional English Melody
Arranged by S. F. L.

1. This is my Fa-ther's world, And to my lis-tening ears All
2. This is my Fa-ther's world, The birds their car-ols raise, The
3. This is my Fa-ther's world, O let me ne'er for-get That

na-ture sings, and round me rings The mu-sic of the spheres.
morn-ing light, the lil-y white, De-clare their Mak-er's praise.
though the wrong seems oft so strong, God is the Rul-er yet.

This is my Fa-ther's world: I rest me in the thought Of
This is my Fa-ther's world: He shines in all that's fair; In the
This is my Fa-ther's world: The bat-tle is not done; Je-

rocks and trees, of skies and seas—His hand the won-ders wrought.
rus-tling grass I hear Him pass, He speaks to me ev-ery-where.
sus who died shall be sat-is-fied, And earth and heaven be one. A-MEN.

The Spacious Firmament

Joseph Addison   CREATION   Franz Joseph Haydn

1. The spa-cious fir-ma-ment on high, With all the blue, e-the-real sky, And span-gled heavens, a shin-ing frame, Their great O-rig-i-nal pro-claim: Th'un-wea-ried sun, from day to day, Does his Cre-a-tor's power dis-play; And pub-lish-es to ev-ery land The work of an al-might-y hand.

2. Soon as the eve-ning shades pre-vail, The moon takes up the won-drous tale; And night-ly, to the lis-tening earth, Re-peats the sto-ry of her birth; While all the stars that round her burn, And all the plan-ets in their turn, Con-firm the ti-dings as they roll, And spread the truth from pole to pole.

3. What though, in sol-emn si-lence, all Move round the dark ter-res-trial ball? What though no re-al voice nor sound A-mid their ra-diant orbs be found? In rea-son's ear they all re-joice, And ut-ter forth a glo-rious voice, For-ev-er sing-ing as they shine, "The hand that made us is di-vine." A-MEN.

39 O God, Our Help

From Psalm 90
Isaac Watts

ST. ANNE

William Croft

1. O God, our help in a - ges past, Our hope for years to come,
2. Un - der the shad - ow of Thy throne Still may we dwell se - cure;
3. Be - fore the hills in or - der stood, Or earth re - ceived her frame,
4. Time, like an ev - er - roll - ing stream, Bears all its sons a - way;
5. Our God, our help in a - ges past, Our hope for years to come,

O shel - ter from the storm-y blast, And our e - ter - nal home!
Suf - fi - cient is Thine arm a - lone, And our de - fense is sure.
From ev - er - last - ing Thou art God, To end-less years the same.
They fly, for - got - ten, as a dream Dies at the ope - ning day.
Be Thou our guide while life shall last, And our e - ter - nal home. A-MEN.

40 When All Thy Mercies, O My God

Joseph Addison

MANOAH

Francis J. Haydn

1. When all Thy mer - cies, O my God, My ris - ing soul sur - veys,
2. Un-num-bered com-forts to my soul, Thy ten - der care be - stowed,
3. Ten thou-sand thou-sand pre-cious gifts My dai - ly thanks em - ploy;
4. Through all e - ter - ni - ty to Thee A joy - ful song I'll raise;

Trans-port-ed with the view, I'm lost In won-der, love, and praise.
Be - fore my in-fant heart could know From whom those comforts flowed.
Nor is the least a cheer-ful heart That tastes those gifts with joy.
But oh, e - ter - ni - ty's too short To ut - ter all Thy praise! A-MEN.

There's a Song in the Air

STARLIGHT

Josiah G. Holland

Carl F. Crusius

1. There's a song in the air! There's a star in the sky!
2. There's a tu - mult of joy O'er the won - der - ful birth,
3. In the light of that star Lie the a - ges im - pearled;
4. We re - joice in the light And we ech - o the song

There's a moth - er's deep prayer, And a ba - by's low cry!
For the Vir - gin's sweet boy Is the Lord of the earth.
And that song from a - far Has swept o - ver the world.
That comes down through the night From the heav - en - ly throng.

And the star rains its fire while the beau - ti [- ful sing,
Ay! the star rains its fire while the beau - ti - ful sing,
Ev - 'ry heart is a - flame, and the beau - ti - ful sing
Ay! we shout to the love - ly E - van - gel they bring,

For the man - ger of Beth - le - hem cra - dles a King!
For the man - ger of Beth - le - hem cra - dles a King!
In the homes of the na - tions that Je - sus is King!
And we greet in His cra - dle our Sav - iour and King!

42   It Came upon the Midnight Clear

CAROL

Edmund H. Sears   Richard S. Willis

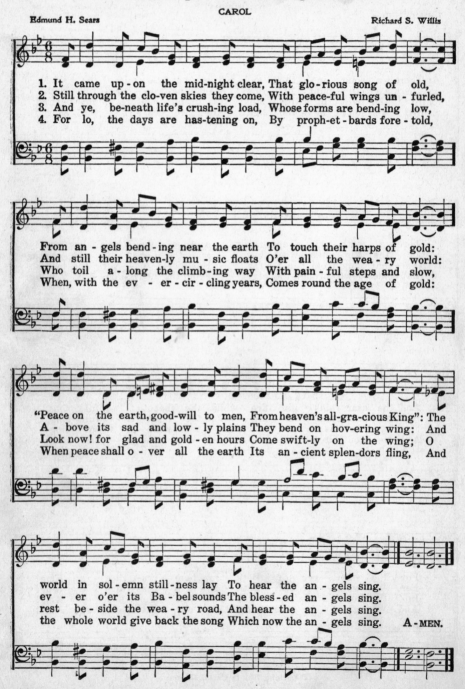

1. It came up - on the mid-night clear, That glo - rious song of old,
2. Still through the clo-ven skies they come, With peace-ful wings un - furled,
3. And ye, be-neath life's crush-ing load, Whose forms are bend-ing low,
4. For lo, the days are has-tening on, By proph-et - bards fore - told,

From an - gels bend-ing near the earth To touch their harps of gold:
And still their heaven-ly mu - sic floats O'er all the wea - ry world:
Who toil a - long the climb-ing way With pain - ful steps and slow,
When, with the ev - er - cir - cling years, Comes round the age of gold:

"Peace on the earth, good-will to men, From heaven's all-gra-cious King": The
A - bove its sad and low - ly plains They bend on hov-ering wing: And
Look now! for glad and gold - en hours Come swift-ly on the wing; O
When peace shall o - ver all the earth Its an - cient splen-dors fling, And

world in sol - emn still - ness lay To hear the an - gels sing.
ev - er o'er its Ba - bel sounds The bless - ed an - gels sing.
rest be - side the wea - ry road, And hear the an - gels sing.
the whole world give back the song Which now the an - gels sing. A - MEN.

Hark, the Herald Angels Sing

MENDELSSOHN

Charles Wesley

Felix Mendelssohn-Bartholdy
Arr. by William S. Cummings

1. Hark! the her - ald an - gels sing, "Glo - ry to the new - born King:
2. Christ, by high - est heaven a - dored; Christ, the Ev - er - last - ing Lord!
3. Hail the heaven-born Prince of Peace! Hail the Sun of Right-eous - ness!

Peace on earth, and mer - cy mild, God and sin - ners rec - on - ciled!"
Late in time be - hold Him come, Off - spring of the Vir - gin's womb:
Light and life to all He brings, Risen with heal - ing in His wings.

Joy - ful, all ye na - tions, rise, Join the tri - umph of the skies;
Veiled in flesh the God - head see; Hail th' In - car - nate De - i - ty,
Mild He lays His glo - ry by, Born that man no more may die,

With th' an - gel - ic host pro-claim, "Christ is born in Beth - le - hem!"
Pleased as man with men to dwell, Je - sus, our Em-man - u - el.
Born to raise the sons of earth, Born to give them sec - ond birth.

Hark! the her - ald an - gels sing, "Glo - ry to the new-born King." A - MEN.

44 The First Noel the Angel Did Say

Old English Carol THE FIRST NOEL.* With Refrain Traditional

1. The first No - el the an - gel did say Was to cer - tain poor
2. They look - ed up and saw a star Shin-ing in the
3. And by the light of that same star, Three wise - men
4. This star drew nigh to the north-west, O'er Beth - le -
5. Then en - tered in those wise - men three, Full rev - er - ent -

shepherds in fields as they lay; In fields where they lay keep-ing their
east, be - yond them far, And to the earth it gave great
came from coun - try far; To seek for a king was their in -
hem it took its rest, And there it did both stop and
ly up - on the knee, And of - fered there, in His pres -

sheep, On a cold win-ter's night that was so deep.
light, And so it con - tin - ued both day and night.
tent, And to fol-low the star wher - ev - er it went.
stay, Right o - ver the place where Je - sus lay.
ence, Their gold, and myrrh, and frank - in - cense.

REFRAIN

No - el, No - el, No - el, No - el, Born is the King of Is - ra - el. A - MEN.

*Noël. From the French "nouvelles," "news;" hence the "good news" [of Christmas].

O Come, All Ye Faithful

ADESTE FIDELES

Latin Hymn, 17th century
Tr. by Frederick Oakeley

Wade's "Cantus Diversi"

1. O come, all ye faith-ful, Joy-ful and tri-um-phant,
2. Sing, choirs of an-gels, Sing in ex-ul-ta-tion!
3. Yea, Lord, we greet Thee, Born this hap-py morn-ing,

O come ye, O come ye to Beth-le-hem!
O sing, all ye bright hosts of heaven a-bove;
Je-sus, to Thee be all glo-ry given;

Come and be-hold Him, Born the King of an-gels;
Glo-ry to God, all Glo-ry in the high-est;
Word of the Fa-ther, Now in flesh ap-pear-ing;

REFRAIN

O come, let us a-dore Him, O come, let us a-dore Him,

O come, let us a-dore Him, Christ the Lord. A-MEN.

46 Silent Night! Holy Night!

STILLE NACHT

Freely translated from
Joseph Mohr

Franz Gruber

1. Si - lent night, ho - ly night, All is calm, all is bright, Round yon
2. Si - lent night, ho - ly night, Dark-ness flies, and all is light: Shep-herds
3. Si - lent night, ho - ly night, Guid-ing Star, O lend thy light; See the
4. Si - lent night, ho - ly night, Wondrous Star, O lend thy light; With the

Vir - gin Moth-er and Child; Ho - ly In - fant, so ten - der and mild,
hear the an - gels sing, "Al - le - lu - - ia! hail the King!
east - ern wise men bring Gifts and hom - age to our King;
an - gels let us sing Al - le - lu - - ia to our King!

Sleeps in heav - en - ly peace, Sleeps in heav - en - ly peace.
Je - sus, the Sav-iour, is here, Je-sus, the Sav-iour, is here."
Je - sus, the Sav-iour, is here, Je-sus, the Sav-iour, is here.
Je - sus, our Sav-iour, is here, Je-sus, our Sav-iour, is here. A - MEN.

47 O Little Town of Bethlehem

ST. LOUIS

Phillips Brooks

Lewis H. Redner

1. O lit-tle town of Beth-le-hem, How still we see thee lie! A - bove thy deep and
2. For Christ is born of Ma - ry, And gathered all a - bove, While mortals sleep, the
3. How si-lent-ly, how si-lent-ly, The wondrous gift is given! So God im-parts to
4. O ho-ly Child of Beth-le-hem! De-scend to us, we pray; Cast out our sin, and

O Little Town of Bethlehem

dreamless sleep The si - lent stars go by. Yet in thy dark streets shineth The ev - er -
an - gels keep Their watch of wondering love. O morn-ing stars, to-geth-er Proclaim the
human hearts The blessings of His heaven. No ear may hear His com-ing, But in this
en - ter in; Be born in us to - day. We hear the Christmas an-gels The great glad

last-ing Light; The hopes and fears of all the years Are met in thee to-night.
ho - ly birth! And prais-es sing to God the King, And peace to men on earth.
world of sin, Where meek souls will receive Him still, The dear Christ enters in.
ti - dings tell; O come to us, a - bide with us, Our Lord Em-man-u - el. A-MEN.

Jesus, the Very Thought of Thee   48

Bernard of Clairvaux
Trans. by Edward Caswall

ST. AGNES

John B. Dykes

1. Je - sus, the ver - y thought of Thee With sweet-ness fills my breast;
2. Nor voice can sing, nor heart can frame, Nor can the mem-ory find
3. O Hope of ev - ery con - trite heart, O Joy of all the meek,
4. But what to those who find? Ah! this Nor tongue nor pen can show,

But sweet-er far Thy face to see, And in Thy pres-ence rest.
A sweet-er sound than Thy blest name, O Sav-iour of man-kind!
To those who fall, how kind Thou art! How good to those who seek!
The love of Je - sus, what it is None but His loved ones know. A - MEN.

Joy to the World!

Isaac Watts   ANTIOCH   George F. Handel

1. Joy to the world! the Lord is come; Let earth re-
2. Joy to the earth! the Sav - iour reigns; Let men their
3. No more let sins and sor - rows grow, Nor thorns in-
4. He rules the world with truth and grace, And makes the

ceive her King; Let ev - ery heart pre - pare Him room,
songs em - ploy; While fields and floods, rocks, hills, and plains,
fest the ground; He comes to make His bless - ings flow
na - tions prove The glo - ries of His right - eous - ness,

And heaven and na - ture sing, And heaven and na - ture
Re - peat the sound - ing joy, Re - peat the sound - ing
Far as the curse is found, Far as the curse is
And won - ders of His love, And won - ders of His

1. And heaven and na - ture sing,.....................

And

sing, And heaven, and heaven and na - ture sing.
joy, Re - peat, re - peat the sound - ing joy.
found, Far as, far as the curse is found.
love, And won - ders, won - ders of His love. A - MEN.

heaven and na - ture sing,

We Three Kings of Orient Are

KINGS OF ORIENT

John H. Hopkins

John H. Hopkins

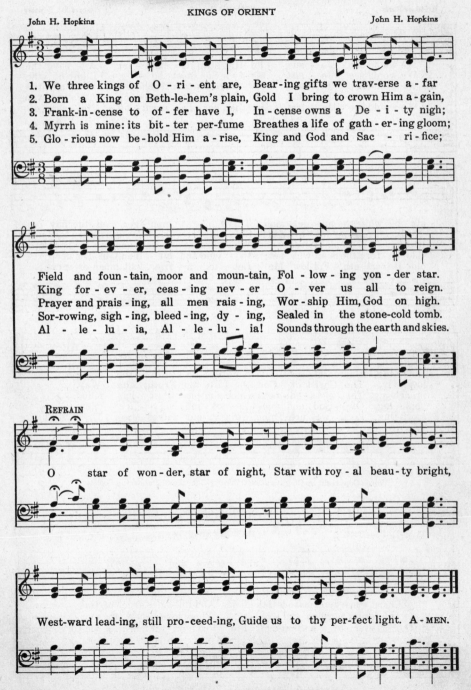

1. We three kings of O - ri - ent are, Bear-ing gifts we trav-erse a - far
2. Born a King on Beth-le-hem's plain, Gold I bring to crown Him a - gain,
3. Frank-in-cense to of - fer have I, In - cense owns a De - i - ty nigh;
4. Myrrh is mine: its bit - ter per-fume Breathes a life of gath - er-ing gloom;
5. Glo - rious now be - hold Him a - rise, King and God and Sac - ri -fice;

Field and foun-tain, moor and moun-tain, Fol - low - ing yon - der star.
King for - ev - er, ceas - ing nev - er O - ver us all to reign.
Prayer and prais - ing, all men rais - ing, Wor-ship Him, God on high.
Sor-rowing, sigh - ing, bleed - ing, dy - ing, Sealed in the stone-cold tomb.
Al - le - lu - ia, Al - le - lu - ia! Sounds through the earth and skies.

REFRAIN

O star of won - der, star of night, Star with roy - al beau - ty bright,

West-ward lead-ing, still pro-ceed-ing, Guide us to thy per-fect light. A - MEN.

51 We Would See Jesus

J. Edgar Park   CUSHMAN   Herbert B. Turner

1. We would see Je - sus, lo! His star is shin - ing A - bove the
2. We would see Je - sus, Ma-ry's Son most ho - ly, Light of the
3. We would see Je - sus, on the moun-tain teach - ing, With all the
4. We would see Je - sus, in His work of heal - ing, At e - ven-
5. We would see Je - sus, in the ear - ly morn - ing, Still as of

sta - ble while the an - gels sing; There in a man - ger, on the hay re-
vil - lage life from day to day; Shin - ing re-vealed through ev-ery task most
lis-tening peo-ple gath-ered round; While birds and flowers and sky a - bove are
tide be - fore the sun was set; Di - vine and hu - man, in His deep re-
old He call-eth, "Fol-low Me"; Let us a - rise, all mean-er serv - ice

clin - ing, Haste, let us lay our gifts be - fore the King.
low - ly, The Christ of God, the Life, the Truth, the Way.
preach-ing, The bless - ed - ness which sim-ple trust has found.
veal - ing, Of God and man in lov - ing serv - ice met.
scorn-ing, Lord, we are Thine, we give our-selves to Thee. A - MEN.

52 O Jesus, Youth of Nazareth

Ferdinand Q. Blanchard   EATON   George W. Chadwick

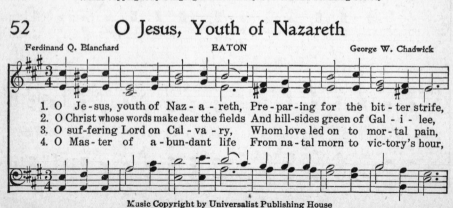

1. O Je - sus, youth of Naz - a - reth, Pre - par-ing for the bit - ter strife,
2. O Christ whose words make dear the fields And hill-sides green of Gal - i - lee,
3. O suf - fering Lord on Cal - va - ry, Whom love led on to mor - tal pain,
4. O Mas - ter of a - bun-dant life From na - tal morn to vic-tory's hour,

O Jesus, Youth of Nazareth

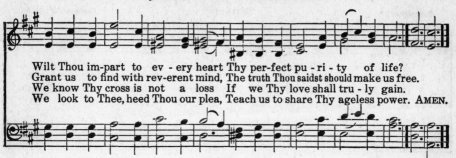

Wilt Thou im-part to ev - ery heart Thy per-fect pu - ri - ty of life?
Grant us to find with rev-erent mind, The truth Thou saidst should make us free.
We know Thy cross is not a loss If we Thy love shall tru - ly gain.
We look to Thee, heed Thou our plea, Teach us to share Thy ageless power. AMEN.

O Son of Man, Our Hero Strong and Tender 53

Frank Fletcher MORNING STAR John P. Harding

1. O Son of man, our he - ro strong and ten - der, Whose serv-ants
2. O feet so strong to climb the path of du - ty, O lips di-
3. Lov - er of chil - dren, boy-hood's in - spi - ra - tion, Of all man-
4. Not in our fail - ures on - ly and our sad - ness We seek Thy

are the brave in all the earth, Our liv - ing sac - ri - fice to
vine that taught the words of truth, Kind eyes that marked the lil - ies
kind the Serv - ant and the King, O Lord of joy and hope and
pres - ence, Com - fort - er and Friend; O rich-man's guest, be with us

Thee we ren - der, Who shar-est all our sor - row, all our mirth.
in their beau - ty, And heart that kin - dled at the zeal of youth.
con - so - la - tion, To Thee our fears and joys and hopes we bring.
in our glad - ness, O poor-man's mate, our dai - ly tasks at - tend! A-MEN.

Words used by permission of Frank Fletcher

54   O Jesus, Once a Nazareth Boy

Anonymous   SERAPH   Gottfried W. Fink

1. O Je - sus, once a Naz - areth boy, And tempt - ed like as we,
2. O Je - sus, Prince of life and truth, Be - neath Thy ban - ner bright.
3. In ser - ried ranks, with fear - less tread, O Cap - tain of us all,

All in - ward foes help us de - stroy And spot - less all to be.
We ded - i - cate our strength and youth To bat - tle for the right;
Thy glo - ry on our ban - ners shed, We an - swer to Thy call;

We trust Thee for the grace to win The high, vic - to - rious goal,
We give our lives with glad in - tent To serve the world and Thee,
And where the fierc - est bat - tles press A - gainst the hosts of sin,

Where pu - ri - ty shall con - quer sin In Christ-like self - con - trol.
To die, to suf - fer and be spent To set our broth-ers free.
To res - cue those in dire dis - tress We glad - ly en - ter in. A - MEN.

My Master Was a Worker

William G. Tarrant   ELLACOMBE   Gesang Buch der Herzogl.

1. My Mas-ter was a work - er, With dai-ly work to do,
2. My Mas-ter was a com - rade, A trust-y friend and true,
3. My Mas-ter was a help - er, The woes of life He knew,
4. Then, broth-ers brave and man - ly, To-geth-er let us be,

And he who would be like Him Must be a work-er too.
And he who would be like Him Must be a com-rade too;
And he who would be like Him Must be a help-er too;
For He, who is our Mas - ter, The Man of men was He;

Then wel-come hon-est la - - bor, And hon-est la-bor's fare,
In hap-py hours of sing - ing, In si-lent hours of care,
The bur-den will grow light - er, If each will take a share,
The men who would be like Him Are want-ed ev-ery-where,

For where there is a work - er The Mas-ter's man is there.
Where goes a loy-al com - rade, The Mas-ter's man is there.
And where there is a help - er The Mas-ter's man is there.
And where they love each oth - er The Mas-ter's men are there. A-MEN.

56   O Master-Workman of the Race

SERAPH

Jay T. Stocking

Gottfried W. Fink

1. O Mas-ter-Work-man of the race, Thou Man of Gal-i-lee,
2. O Car-pen-ter of Naz-a-reth, Build-er of life di-vine,
3. O Thou who dost the vi-sion send And giv-est each his task,

Who with the eyes of ear-ly youth E-ter-nal things didst see,
Who shap-est man to God's own law, Thy-self the fair de-sign,
And with the task suf-fi-cient strength, Show us Thy will, we ask;

We thank Thee for Thy boy-hood faith That shone Thy whole life through;
Build us a tower of Christ-like height, That we the land may view,
Give us a con-science bold and good, Give us a pur-pose true,

"Did ye not know it is My work My Fa-ther's work to do?"
And see like Thee our no-blest work Our Fa-ther's work to do.
That it may be our high-est joy Our Fa-ther's work to do. A-MEN.

Jesus, Thou Divine Companion

LOVE DIVINE

Henry van Dyke

George F. Le Jeune

57

1. Je - sus, Thou di - vine Com-pan - ion, By Thy low - ly hu - man birth
2. They who tread the path of la - bor Fol - low where Thy feet have trod;
3. Ev - ery task, how - ev - er sim - ple, Sets the soul that does it free;

Thou hast come to join the work - ers, Bur - den - bear - ers of the earth.
They who work with - out com-plain - ing Do the ho - ly will of God.
Ev - ery deed of love and kind - ness Done to man is done to Thee.

Thou, the Car - pen - ter of Naz-areth, Toil - ing for Thy dai - ly food,
Thou, the Peace that pass - eth knowl-edge, Dwell-est in the dai - ly strife;
Je - sus, Thou di - vine Com - pan - ion, Help us all to work our best;

By Thy pa-tience and Thy cour-age, Thou hast taught us toil is good.
Thou, the Bread of heaven, art bro - ken, In the sac - ra - ment of life.
Bless us in our dai - ly la - bor, Lead us to our Sab-bath rest. A-MEN.

58 Galilee, Bright Galilee

William F. Sherwin   GALILEE (Sherwin)   William F. Sherwin

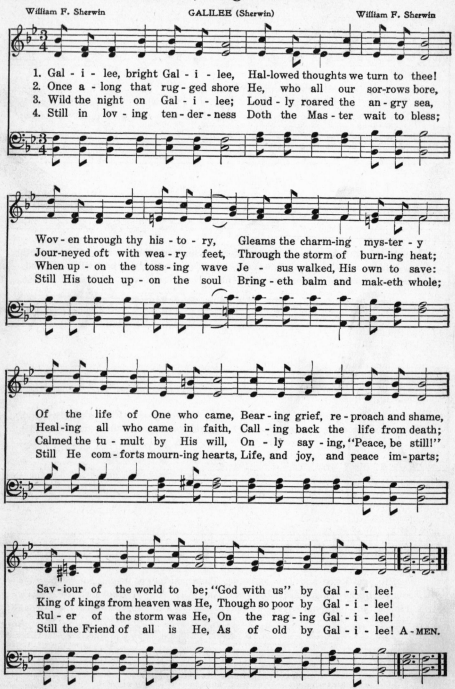

1. Gal - i - lee, bright Gal - i - lee, Hal-lowed thoughts we turn to thee!
2. Once a - long that rug - ged shore He, who all our sor-rows bore,
3. Wild the night on Gal - i - lee; Loud - ly roared the an - gry sea,
4. Still in lov - ing ten - der - ness Doth the Mas - ter wait to bless;

Wov - en through thy his - to - ry, Gleams the charm - ing mys-ter - y
Jour-neyed oft with wea - ry feet, Through the storm of burn-ing heat;
When up - on the toss - ing wave Je - sus walked, His own to save:
Still His touch up - on the soul Bring - eth balm and mak-eth whole;

Of the life of One who came, Bear - ing grief, re - proach and shame,
Heal-ing all who came in faith, Call - ing back the life from death;
Calmed the tu - mult by His will, On - ly say - ing, "Peace, be still!"
Still He com - forts mourn-ing hearts, Life, and joy, and peace im-parts;

Sav - iour of the world to be; "God with us" by Gal - i - lee!
King of kings from heaven was He, Though so poor by Gal - i - lee!
Rul - er of the storm was He, On the rag - ing Gal - i - lee!
Still the Friend of all is He, As of old by Gal - i - lee! A - MEN.

I Bind My Heart This Tide

FEALTY

Laughlan MacLean Watt

Grace Wilbur Conant

1. I bind my heart this tide To the Gal - i - le - an's side,
2. I bind my heart in thrall To the God, the Lord of all,

To the wounds of Cal - va - ry,— To the Christ who died for me.
To the God, the poor man's Friend, And the Christ whom He did send.

I bind my soul this day To the broth-er far a - way,
I bind my - self to peace, To make strife and en - vy cease,

And the broth-er near at hand, In this town, and in this land.
God! knit Thou sure the cord Of my thral-dom to my Lord. A - MEN.

60 Into the Woods My Master Went

LANIER

Sidney Lanier

Peter C. Lutkin

1. In - to the woods my Mas - ter went, Clean for-spent, for - spent;
2. Out of the woods my Mas - ter went, And He was well con - tent;

In - to the woods my Mas - ter came, For-spent with love and shame. But the
Out of the woods my Mas - ter came, Con - tent with death and shame. When

ol - ives they were not blind to Him, The lit - tle gray leaves were kind to Him,
death and shame would woo Him last, From un - der the trees they drew Him last,

The thorn-tree had a mind to Him, When in - to the woods He came.
'Twas on a tree they slew Him last, When out of the woods He came. A-MEN.

In the Cross of Christ

John Bowring · RATHBUN · Ithamar Conkey

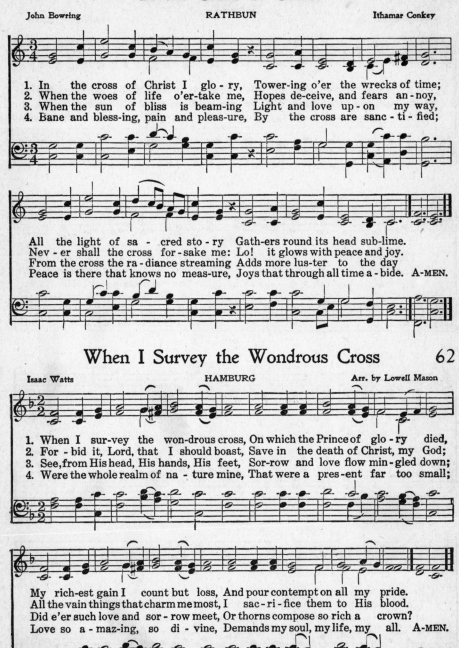

1. In the cross of Christ I glo - ry, Tower-ing o'er the wrecks of time;
2. When the woes of life o'er-take me, Hopes de-ceive, and fears an - noy,
3. When the sun of bliss is beam-ing Light and love up - on my way,
4. Bane and bless-ing, pain and pleas-ure, By the cross are sanc - ti - fied;

All the light of sa - cred sto - ry Gath-ers round its head sub-lime.
Nev - er shall the cross for - sake me: Lo! it glows with peace and joy.
From the cross the ra - diance streaming Adds more lus-ter to the day
Peace is there that knows no meas-ure, Joys that through all time a - bide. A-MEN.

When I Survey the Wondrous Cross

Isaac Watts · HAMBURG · Arr. by Lowell Mason

1. When I sur-vey the won-drous cross, On which the Prince of glo - ry died,
2. For - bid it, Lord, that I should boast, Save in the death of Christ, my God;
3. See, from His head, His hands, His feet, Sor-row and love flow min - gled down;
4. Were the whole realm of na - ture mine, That were a pres-ent far too small;

My rich-est gain I count but loss, And pour contempt on all my pride.
All the vain things that charm me most, I sac - ri - fice them to His blood.
Did e'er such love and sor - row meet, Or thorns compose so rich a crown?
Love so a - maz-ing, so di - vine, Demands my soul, my life, my all. A-MEN.

63 Beneath the Cross of Jesus

ST. CHRISTOPHER

Elizabeth C. Clephane

Frederick C. Maker

1. Be - neath the cross of Je - sus I fain would take my stand—
2. Up - on that cross of Je - sus Mine eye at times can see
3. I take, O cross, thy shad - ow For my a - bid - ing - place;

The shad - ow of a might - y Rock With - in a wea - ry land;
The ver - y dy - ing form of One Who suf - fered there for me;
I ask no oth - er sun-shine than The sun - shine of His face;

A home with - in the wil - der - ness, A rest up - on the way,
And from my smit - ten heart with tears Two won - ders I con - fess—
Con - tent to let the world go by, To know no gain nor loss,

From the burn-ing of the noon-tide heat, And the bur-den of the day.
The won - ders of re-deem-ing love And my un-wor-thi-ness.
My sin - ful self my on - ly shame, My glo - ry all the cross. A-MEN.

There Is a Green Hill Far Away

Cecil F. Alexander

George C. Stebbins

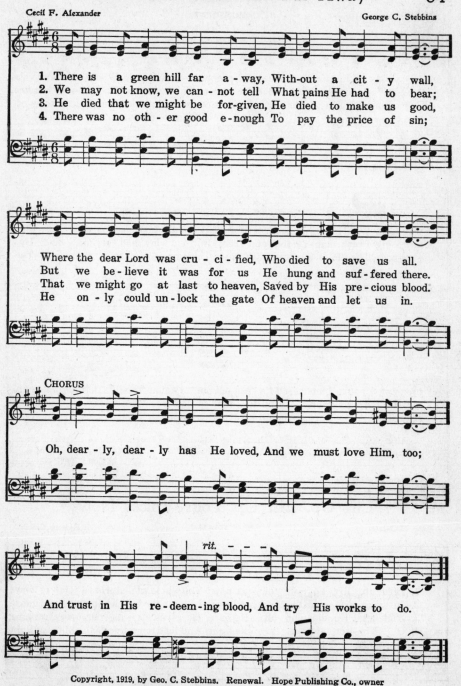

1. There is a green hill far a-way, With-out a cit-y wall,
2. We may not know, we can-not tell What pains He had to bear;
3. He died that we might be for-given, He died to make us good,
4. There was no oth-er good e-nough To pay the price of sin;

Where the dear Lord was cru-ci-fied, Who died to save us all.
But we be-lieve it was for us He hung and suf-fered there.
That we might go at last to heaven, Saved by His pre-cious blood.
He on-ly could un-lock the gate Of heaven and let us in.

CHORUS

Oh, dear-ly, dear-ly has He loved, And we must love Him, too;

rit.

And trust in His re-deem-ing blood, And try His works to do.

65 O Day of Light and Gladness

Frederick Lucian Hosmer   LANCASHIRE   Henry Smart

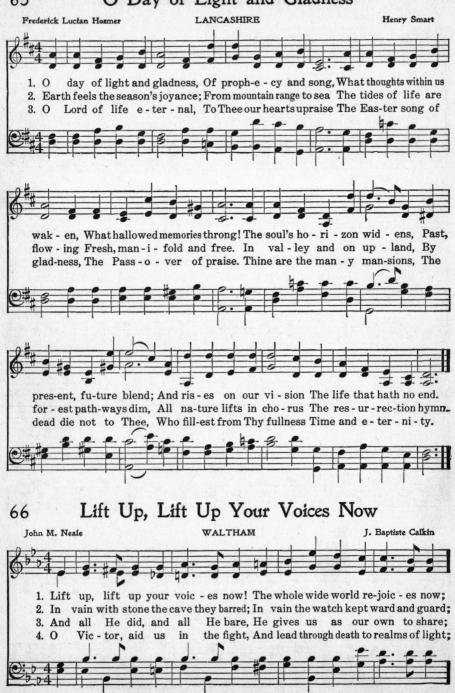

1. O day of light and gladness, Of proph-e-cy and song, What thoughts within us
2. Earth feels the season's joyance; From mountain range to sea The tides of life are
3. O Lord of life e-ter-nal, To Thee our hearts upraise The Eas-ter song of

wak-en, What hallowed memories throng! The soul's ho-ri-zon wid-ens, Past,
flow-ing Fresh, man-i-fold and free. In val-ley and on up-land, By
glad-ness, The Pass-o-ver of praise. Thine are the man-y man-sions, The

pres-ent, fu-ture blend; And ris-es on our vi-sion The life that hath no end.
for-est path-ways dim, All na-ture lifts in cho-rus The res-ur-rec-tion hymn.
dead die not to Thee, Who fill-est from Thy fullness Time and e-ter-ni-ty.

66 Lift Up, Lift Up Your Voices Now

John M. Neale   WALTHAM   J. Baptiste Calkin

1. Lift up, lift up your voic-es now! The whole wide world re-joic-es now;
2. In vain with stone the cave they barred; In vain the watch kept ward and guard;
3. And all He did, and all He bare, He gives us as our own to share;
4. O Vic-tor, aid us in the fight, And lead through death to realms of light;

Lift Up, Lift Up Your Voices Now

The Lord hath triumphed glo-rious-ly, The Lord shall reign vic-to-rious-ly.
Ma - jes - tic from the spoil-ed tomb, In pomp of tri-umph Christ is come.
And hope, and joy, and peace be-gin, For Christ has won, and man shall win.
We safe - ly pass where Thou hast trod; In Thee we die to rise to God. A-MEN

The Strife Is O'er 67

VICTORY With Alleluia

Anon. (Latin) tr. by Francis Pott

From "Palestrina"
Arr. by William H. Monk

Al - le - lu - ia! Al - le - lu - ia! Al - le - lu - ia!

Org.

1. The strife is o'er, the bat - tle done; The vic - to - ry of life is
2. The powers of death have done their worst, But Christ their le - gions hath dis-
3. The three sad days are quick-ly sped; He ris - es glo-rious from the
4. Lord, by the stripes which wound-ed Thee, From death's dread sting Thy serv-ants

D. S.

won; The song of tri-umph has be - gun. Al-le-lu - ia!
persed; Let shouts of ho - ly joy out-burst. Al-le-lu - ia!
dead; All glo - ry to our ris - en Head! Al-le-lu - ia!
free, That we may live and sing to Thee, Al-le-lu - ia! A-MEN.

Christ the Lord Is Risen Today

Charles Wesley WORGAN Arr. from "Lyra Davidica"

1. Christ the Lord is risen to - day, Al - - - le - lu - ia!
2. Love's re - deem - ing work is done, Al - - - le - lu - ia!
3. Lives a - gain our glo - rious King; Al - - - le - lu - ia!
4. Soar we now where Christ has led, Al - - - le - le - ia!

Sons of men and an - gels say: Al - - - le - lu - ia!
Fought the fight, the bat - tle won; Al - - - le - lu - ia!
Where, O death, is now thy sting? Al - - - le - lu - ia!
Fol - lowing our ex - alt - ed Head; Al - - - le - lu - ia!

Raise your joys and tri - umphs high, Al - - - le - lu - ia!
Death in vain for - bids Him rise; Al - - - le - lu - ia!
Dy - ing once, He all doth save: Al - - - le - lu - ia!
Made like Him, like Him we rise; Al - - - le - lu - ia!

Sing, ye heavens, and earth re - ply, Al - - - le - lu - ia!
Christ has o - pened Par - a - dise. Al - - - le - lu - ia!
Where thy vic - to - ry, O grave? Al - - - le - lu - ia!
Ours the cross, the grave, the skies. Al - - - le - lu - ia! A-MEN.

The Day of Resurrection

SALVATORI

John of Damascus
Tr. by John M. Neale

Arr. from Haydn

1. The day of res-ur-rec-tion! Earth, tell it out a-broad;
2. Our hearts be pure from e-vil, That we may see a-right
3. Now let the heavens be joy-ful, And earth her song be-gin,

The Pass-o-ver of glad-ness, The Pass-o-ver of God!
The Lord in rays e-ter-nal Of res-ur-rec-tion light;
The round world keeps high tri-umph, And all that is there-in;

From death to life e-ter-nal, From earth un-to the sky,
And, lis-tening to His ac-cents, May hear so calm and plain
Let all things seen and un-seen Their notes of glad-ness blend,

Our Christ hath brought us o-ver With hymns of vic-to-ry.
His own "All hail," and, hear-ing, May raise the vic-tor strain.
For Christ the Lord hath ris-en, Our Joy that hath no end. A-MEN.

70 We Bear the Strain of Earthly Care

Ozora Stearns Davis   SERENITY   Arranged from William V. Wallace

1. We bear the strain of earth - ly care, But bear it not a - lone;
2. Through din of mar - ket, whirl of wheels, And thrust of driv - ing trade,
3. The com - mon hopes that make us men Were His in Gal - i - lee;
4. Our broth - er - hood still rests in Him, The Broth - er of us all,

Be - side us walks our broth-er Christ And makes our task His own.
We fol - low where the Mas-ter leads, Se - rene and un - a - fraid.
The tasks He gives are those He gave Be - side the rest - less sea.
And o'er the cen-turies still we hear The Mas-ter's win-some call. A - MEN.

71 Immortal Love, Forever Full

John G. Whittier   SERENITY   Arranged from William V. Wallace

1. Im - mor - tal Love, for - ev - er full, For - ev - er flow - ing free,
2. We may not climb the heaven - ly steeps To bring the Lord Christ down;
3. But warm, sweet, ten-der, e - ven yet A pres - ent help is He;
4. The heal - ing of His seam - less dress Is by our beds of pain;
5. O Lord and Mas - ter of us all, What-e'er our name or sign,

For - ev - er shared, for - ev - er whole, A nev - er - ebb - ing sea.
In vain we search the low - est deeps, For Him no depths can drown.
And faith has still its Ol - i - vet, And love its Gal - i - lee.
We touch Him in life's throng and press And we are whole a - gain.
We own Thy sway, we hear Thy call, We test our lives by Thine. A - MEN.

O Life That Maketh All Things New 72

Samuel Longfellow THANKSGIVING. L. M. Francis Reginald Statham

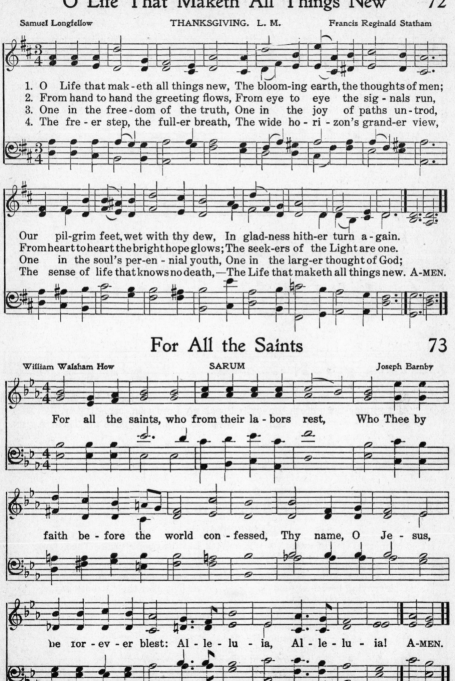

1. O Life that mak - eth all things new, The bloom-ing earth, the thoughts of men;
2. From hand to hand the greeting flows, From eye to eye the sig - nals run,
3. One in the free - dom of the truth, One in the joy of paths un - trod,
4. The fre - er step, the full - er breath, The wide ho - ri - zon's grand-er view,

Our pil-grim feet, wet with thy dew, In glad-ness hith-er turn a - gain.
From heart to heart the bright hope glows; The seek-ers of the Light are one.
One in the soul's per-en - nial youth, One in the larg-er thought of God;
The sense of life that knows no death,—The Life that maketh all things new. A-MEN.

For All the Saints 73

William Walsham How SARUM Joseph Barnby

For all the saints, who from their la - bors rest, Who Thee by

faith be - fore the world con - fessed, Thy name, O Je - sus,

be for - ev - er blest: Al - le - lu - ia, Al - le - lu - ia! A-MEN.

74 Gracious Spirit, Dwell with Me

REDHEAD

Thomas Toke Lynch

Richard Redhead

1. Gra - cious Spir - it, dwell with me; I my - self would gra - cious be;
2. Truth - ful Spir - it, dwell with me; I my - self would truth - ful be;
3. Ho - ly Spir - it, dwell with me; I my - self would ho - ly be;

And with words that help and heal Would Thy life in mine re - veal;
And with wis - dom kind and clear Let Thy life in mine ap - pear;
Sep - a - rate from sin, I would Choose and cher - ish all things good,

And with ac - tions bold and meek Would for Christ my Sav - iour speak.
And with ac - tions broth - er - ly Speak my Lord's sin - cer - i - ty.
And what - ev - er I can be Give to Him who gave me Thee! A-MEN.

75 God of Mercy, God of Grace

Tune: REDHEAD No. 74

1 God of mercy, God of grace,
Show the brightness of Thy face;
Shine upon us, Saviour, shine,
Fill Thy Church with light divine:
And Thy saving health extend
Unto earth's remotest end.

2 Let the people praise Thee, Lord;
Be by all that live adored.
Let the nations shout and sing
Glory to their Saviour King;
At Thy feet their tribute pay,
And Thy holy will obey.

3 Let the people praise Thee, Lord;
Earth shall then her fruits afford;
God to man His blessing give,
Man to God devoted live;
All below, and all above,
One in joy, and light, and love. AMEN.

Psalm 67. Rev. Henry F. Lyte

Spirit of God, Descend upon My Heart 76

MORECAMBE

George Croly

Frederick C. Atkinson

1. Spir - it of God, de - scend up - on my heart;
2. Hast Thou not bid us love Thee, God and King?
3. Teach me to feel that Thou art al - ways nigh;
4. Teach me to love Thee as Thine an - gels love,

Wean it from earth, through all its puls - es move;
All, all Thine own, soul, heart and strength and mind;
Teach me the strug - gles of the soul to bear,
One ho - ly pas - sion fill - ing all my frame;

Stoop to my weak - ness, might - y as Thou art,
I see Thy cross— there teach my heart to cling:
To check the ris - ing doubt, the reb - el sigh;
The bap - tism of the heaven - de - scend - ed Dove,

And make me love Thee as I ought to love.
O let me seek Thee, and O let me find.
Teach me the pa - tience of un - an - swered prayer.
My heart an al - tar, and Thy love the flame. A - MEN.

Christian, Dost Thou See Them

Andrew of Crete
Tr. by James M. Neale

ST. ANDREW OF CRETE

John B. Dykes

1. Chris - tian, dost thou see them On the ho - ly ground,
2. Chris - tian, dost thou feel them, How they work with - in,
3. Chris - tian, dost thou hear them, How they speak thee fair,
4. "Well I know thy trou - ble, O my serv - ant true;

How the powers of dark - ness Com - pass thee a - round?
Striv - ing, tempt - ing, lur - ing, Goad - ing in - to sin?
"Al - ways fast and vig - - il, Al - ways watch and prayer?"
Thou art ver - y wea - ry, I was wea - ry, too;

Chris - tian, up and smite them, Count - ing gain² but loss,
Chris - tian, nev - er trem - ble, Nev - er be down - cast;
Chris - tian, an - swer bold - ly, "While I breathe I pray,"
But that toil shall make thee Some day all Mine own,

In the strength that com - eth By the ho - ly cross.
Gird thee for the bat - tle, Watch and pray and fast.
Peace shall fol - low bat - tle, Night shall end in day.
And the end of sor - row Shall be near My throne." A-MEN.

Holy Spirit, Truth Divine

Samuel Longfellow   MERCY   Louis M. Gottschalk

1. Ho - ly Spir - it, Truth di - vine, Dawn up - on this soul of mine;
2. Ho - ly Spir - it, Love di - vine, Glow with - in this heart of mine;
3. Ho - ly Spir - it, Power di - vine, Fill and nerve this will of mine;
4. Ho - ly Spir - it, Right di - vine, King with - in my con - science reign;
5. Ho - ly Spir - it, Joy di - vine, Glad - den Thou this heart of mine;

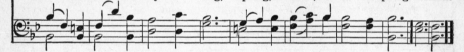

Word of God, and in - ward Light, Wake my spir - it, clear my sight.
Kin - dle ev - ery high de - sire; Per - ish self in Thy pure fire.
By Thee may I strong - ly live, Brave - ly bear, and no - bly strive.
Be my law, and I shall be, Firm - ly bound, for - ev - er free.
In the des - ert ways I sing, "Spring, O Well, for - ev - er spring." AMEN.

Breathe on Me, Breath of God   79

Edwin Hatch   TRENTHAM   Robert Jackson

1. Breathe on me, Breath of God, Fill me with life a - new, That I may
2. Breathe on me, Breath of God, Un - til my heart is pure, Un - til with
3. Breathe on me, Breath of God, Till I am whol - ly Thine, Un - til this
4. Breathe on me, Breath of God, So shall I nev - er die, But live with

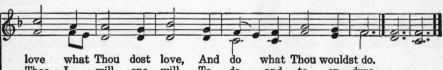

love what Thou dost love, And do what Thou wouldst do.
Thee I will one will, To do and to en - dure.
earth - ly part of me Glows with Thy fire di - vine.
Thee the per - fect life Of Thine e - ter - ni - ty. A - MEN.

Used by permission of Miss Beatrice Hatch and the Oxford University Press

80 Glorious Things of Thee Are Spoken

AUSTRIAN HYMN

John Newton

Franz Joseph Haydn

With exultation

1. Glo-rious things of thee are spo-ken, Zi-on, cit-y of our God;
2. See, the streams of liv-ing wa-ters, Springing from e-ter-nal Love,
3. Round each hab-i-ta-tion hov-ering, See the cloud and fire ap-pear

He whose word can-not be bro-ken Formed thee for His own a-bode:
Well sup-ply thy sons and daugh-ters, And all fear of want re-move:
For a glo-ry and a cov-ering, Show-ing that the Lord is near:

On the Rock of A-ges found-ed, What can shake thy sure re-pose?
Who can faint, while such a riv-er Ev-er flows their thirst to as-suage;
Thus de-riv-ing from their ban-ner Light by night and shade by day,

With sal-va-tion's walls sur-round-ed, Thou mayst smile at all thy foes.
Grace, which, like the Lord the Giv-er, Nev-er fails from age to age?
Safe they feed up-on the man-na Which He gives them when they pray. A-MEN.

O Church of God, Our Solitude Forsaking 81

Rolland W. Schloerb   FINLANDIA   Jean Sibelius

1. O Church of God, our sol - i - tude for - sak - ing, We now u-
nite with all who seek thy way— With those who sing, with
those whose hearts are break-ing, We lift our spir - its as to God we
pray. O Church of God, our love for thee is wak - ing,
We bring our al - le - lu - i - as to - day.

2. O Church of God, like bells at noon - day peal-ing, Thy call has
come to us that we may bring Our strength to serve, to
all the Christ re - veal - ing, In deeds of love and when our hopes take
wing. O Church of God, where sin and pain find heal - ing,
To thee our al - le - lu - i - as we sing.

3. Our spir-it's home, with joy to thee re - turn-ing, Our voic - es
join to sing our high - est praise, For hours of cheer, where
friendship's fires are burn - ing, For strength and peace which glad-den all our
days. O Church of God, for thee our hearts are yearn-ing,
To thee our al - le - lu - i - as we raise. A-MEN.

Words used by permission of Rolland W. Schloerb

82 The Church's One Foundation

Samuel J. Stone   AURELIA   Samuel S. Wesley

1. The Church's one Foun - da - tion Is Je - sus Christ her Lord;
2. E - lect from ev - ery na - tion, Yet one o'er all the earth,
3. 'Mid toil and trib - u - la - tion, And tu - mult of her war,
4. Yet she on earth hath un - ion With God the Three in One,

She is His new cre - a - tion, By wa - ter and the word:
Her char - ter of sal - va - tion, One Lord, one faith, one birth;
She waits the con - sum - ma - tion Of peace for - ev - er - more;
And mys - tic sweet com - mun - ion With those whose rest is won:

From heaven He came and sought her To be His ho - ly Bride;
One ho - ly name she bless - es, Par - takes one ho - ly food,
Till with the vi - sion glo - rious Her long - ing eyes are blest,
O hap - py ones and ho - ly! Lord, give us grace that we,

With His own blood He bought her, And for her life He died.
And to one hope she press - es, With ev - ery grace en - dued.
And the great Church vic - to - rious Shall be the Church at rest.
Like them, the meek and low - ly, On high may dwell with Thee. A-MEN.

I Love Thy Kingdom, Lord

83

Timothy Dwight
ST. THOMAS
Aaron Williams

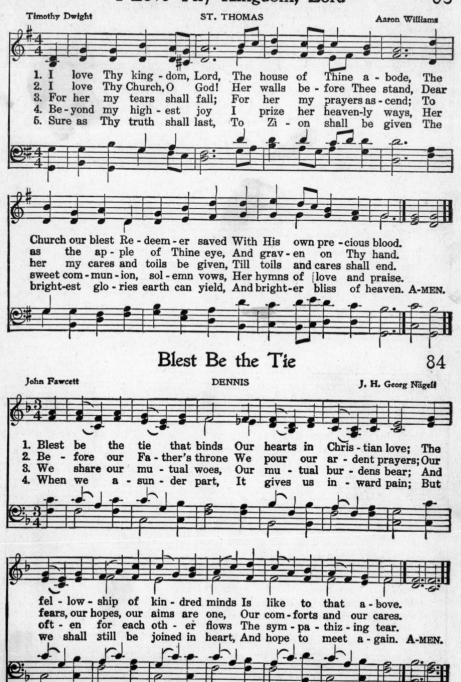

1. I love Thy king-dom, Lord, The house of Thine a-bode, The
2. I love Thy Church, O God! Her walls be-fore Thee stand, Dear
3. For her my tears shall fall; For her my prayers as-cend; To
4. Be-yond my high-est joy I prize her heaven-ly ways, Her
5. Sure as Thy truth shall last, To Zi-on shall be given The

Church our blest Re-deem-er saved With His own pre-cious blood.
as the ap-ple of Thine eye, And grav-en on Thy hand.
her my cares and toils be given, Till toils and cares shall end.
sweet com-mun-ion, sol-emn vows, Her hymns of love and praise.
bright-est glo-ries earth can yield, And bright-er bliss of heaven. A-MEN.

Blest Be the Tie

84

John Fawcett
DENNIS
J. H. Georg Nägeli

1. Blest be the tie that binds Our hearts in Chris-tian love; The
2. Be-fore our Fa-ther's throne We pour our ar-dent prayers; Our
3. We share our mu-tual woes, Our mu-tual bur-dens bear; And
4. When we a-sun-der part, It gives us in-ward pain; But

fel-low-ship of kin-dred minds Is like to that a-bove.
fears, our hopes, our aims are one, Our com-forts and our cares.
oft-en for each oth-er flows The sym-pa-thiz-ing tear.
we shall still be joined in heart, And hope to meet a-gain. A-MEN.

85   Book of Books, Our People's Strength

DESSAU (LIEBSTER JESU)

Percy Dearmer   Johann R. Ahle, Later form

1. Book of books, our peo - ple's strength, States-man's, teach-er's,
2. Thank we those who toiled in thought, Man - y di - verse
3. Praise we God, who hath in - spired Those whose wis - dom

he - ro's treas - ure, Bring - ing free - dom, spread - ing truth,
scrolls com - plet - ing: Po - ets, proph - ets, schol - ars, saints,
still di - rects us; Praise Him for the Word made flesh,

Shed - ding light that none can meas - ure: Wis - dom comes to
Each his word from God re - peat - ing; Till they came, who
For the Spir - it which pro - tects us. Light of Know-ledge,

those who know thee, All the best we have we owe thee.
told the sto - ry Of the Word, and showed His glo - ry.
ev - er burn - ing, Shed on us Thy death-less learn - ing. A - MEN.

Thy Word Is Like a Garden, Lord

SERAPH

Edwin Hodder   Gottfried W. Fink

1. Thy Word is like a gar-den, Lord, With flow-ers bright and fair;
2. Thy Word is like a star-ry host: A thou-sand rays of light
3. O may I love Thy pre-cious Word, May I ex-plore the mine,

And ev-ery one who seeks may pluck A love-ly clus-ter there.
Are seen to guide the trav-el-er, And make his path-way bright.
May I its fra-grant flow-ers glean, May light up-on me shine.

Thy Word is like a deep, deep mine; And jew-els rich and rare
Thy Word is like an ar-mor-y, Where sol-diers may re-pair,
O may I find my ar-mor there, Thy Word my trust-y sword;

Are hid-den in its might-y depths For ev-ery search-er there.
And find, for life's long bat-tle-day, All need-ful weap-ons there.
I'll learn to fight with ev-ery foe The bat-tle of the Lord. A-MEN.

O Word of God Incarnate

William W. How   MUNICH   Würtemberg Gesangbuch

1. O Word of God in-car-nate, O Wis-dom from on high,
2. The Church from her dear Mas-ter Re-ceived the gift di-vine,
3. It float-eth like a ban-ner Be-fore God's host un-furled;
4. O make Thy Church, dear Sav-iour, A lamp of pur-est gold,

O Truth un-changed, un-chang-ing, O Light of our dark sky;
And still that light she lift-eth O'er all the earth to shine.
It shin-eth like a bea-con A-bove the dark-ling world.
To bear be-fore the na-tions Thy true light, as of old.

We praise Thee for the ra-diance That from the hal-lowed page,
It is the gold-en cas-ket, Where gems of truth are stored;
It is the chart and com-pass That o'er life's surg-ing sea,
O teach Thy wan-dering pil-grims By this their path to trace,

A lan-tern to our foot-steps, Shines on from age to age.
It is the heaven-drawn pic-ture Of Christ, the liv-ing Word.
'Mid mists and rocks and quick-sands, Still guides, O Christ, to Thee.
Till, clouds and dark-ness end-ed, They see Thee face to face. A-MEN.

Break Thou the Bread of Life

88

Mary Ann Lathbury   BREAD OF LIFE   William F. Sherwin

1. Break Thou the bread of life, Dear Lord, to me, As Thou didst
2. Bless Thou the truth, dear Lord, To me— to me, As Thou didst
3. Thou art the bread of life, O Lord, to me, Thy ho - ly
4. O send Thy Spir - it, Lord, Now un - to me, That He may

break the loaves Be - side the sea; Be - yond the sa - cred page
bless the bread By Gal - i - lee; Then shall all bond - age cease,
Word the truth That sav - eth me; Give me to eat and live
touch my eyes, And make me see: Show me the truth con-cealed

I seek Thee, Lord, My spir - it pants for Thee, O liv - ing Word.
All fet - ters fall; And I shall find my peace, My All in all.
With Thee a - bove; Teach me to love Thy truth, For Thou art love.
With-in Thy Word, And in Thy Book re-vealed I see Thee Lord. A-MEN.

O Lord, Open Thou Our Eyes

89

John Camidge

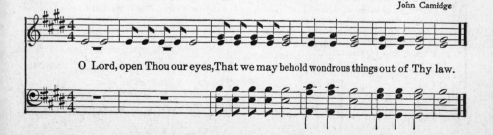

O Lord, open Thou our eyes, That we may behold wondrous things out of Thy law.

90 Lead on, O King Eternal

Ernest W. Shurtleff   LANCASHIRE   Henry Smart

1. Lead on, O King E - ter - nal, The day of march has come;
2. Lead on, O King E - ter - nal, Till sin's fierce war shall cease,
3. Lead on, O King E - ter - nal, We fol - low, not with fears;

Hence-forth in fields of con - quest Thy tents shall be our home.
And ho - li - ness shall whis - per The sweet A - men of peace;
For glad - ness breaks like morn - ing Wher - e'er Thy face ap - pears;

Through days of prep - a - ra - tion Thy grace has made us strong,
For not with swords loud clash - ing, Nor roll of stir - ring drums,
Thy cross is lift - ed o'er us; We jour - ney in its light:

And now, O King E - ter - nal, We lift our bat - tle song.
With deeds of love and mer - cy, The heaven-ly king-dom comes.
The crown a - waits the con - quest; Lead on, O God of might. A-MEN.

91 From Ocean Unto Ocean

Tune: LANCASHIRE No. 90

1 From ocean unto ocean
  Our land shall own Thee, Lord,
And, filled with true devotion,
  Obey Thy sovereign word.
Our prairies and our mountains,
  Forest and fertile field,
Our rivers, lakes, and fountains,
  To Thee shall tribute yield.

2 O Christ, for Thine own glory,
  And for our country's weal,
We humbly plead before Thee,
  Thyself in us reveal;

And may we know, Lord Jesus,
  The touch of Thy dear hand;
And, healed of our diseases,
  The Tempter's power withstand.

3 Our Saviour King, defend us,
  And guide where we should go;
Forth with Thy message send us,
  Thy love and light to show;
Till, fired with true devotion,
  Enkindled by Thy word,
From ocean unto ocean
  Our land shall own Thee Lord. AMEN.

Rev. Robert Murray

O Star of Truth, Down Shining

Minot J. Savage   ALEXANDER   Alexander S. Gibson

1. O star of truth, down shin - ing Through clouds of dust and fear,
2. I know thy bless - ed ra - diance Can nev - er lead a - stray,
3. The bleed - ing feet of mar - tyrs Thy toil - some road have trod;

I ask but 'neath thy guid - ance My path - way may ap - pear.
How - ev - er an - cient cus - tom May tread some oth - er way.
But fires of hu - man pas - sion May light the way to God.

How - ev - er long the jour - ney, How hard so - e'er it be,
E'en if through un - trod des - erts, Or o - ver track - less sea,
Then, though my feet should fal - ter, While I thy beams can see,

Though I be lone and wea - ry, Lead on, I'll fol - low thee!
Though I be lone and wea - ry, Lead on, I'll fol - low thee!
Though I be lone and wea - ry, Lead on, I'll fol - low thee! A-MEN.

93 Thou Art My Shepherd

Elsie Thalheimer
Mrs. M. Scott Haycroft

LYNDE

Thuringian Folksong
Arr. by John B. Cramer

1. Thou art my Shep-herd, Car - ing in ev - ery need, Thy lov - ing
2. Or if my way lie Where storms are rag-ing nigh, Noth - ing can
3. Good - ness and mer - cy Ev - er shall fol - low me, Till by Thy

lamb to feed, Trust-ing Thee still. In the green pastures low, Where liv - ing
ter - ri - fy, I trust Thee still. How can I be a-fraid, While soft - ly
grace I see Thy ho - ly hill; Lord, in that home with Thee, Joy - ful e-

wa - ters flow, Safe by Thy side I go, Fear - ing no ill.
on my head Thy ten - der hand is laid? I fear no ill.
ter - nal - ly, Fold - ed Thy flock shall be, Safe from all ill. A-MEN.

94 Summer Suns Are Glowing

William W. How

RUTH

Samuel Smith

1. Sum - mer suns are glow - ing O - ver land and sea; Hap - py light is
2. God's free mer - cy stream-eth O - ver all the world, And His ban - ner
3. Lord, up - on our blind - ness Thy pure ra - diance pour; For Thy lov - ing
4. We will nev - er doubt Thee, Though Thou veil Thy light; Life is dark with-

Summer Suns Are Glowing

flow - ing, Boun-ti-ful and free; Ev-ery-thing re-joic-es In the
gleam-eth Ev-ery-where un-furled; Broad and deep and glo-rious As the
kind-ness Make us love Thee more: And when clouds are drift-ing Dark a-
out Thee, Death with Thee is bright. Light of light, shine o'er us On our

mel-low rays, All earth's thousand voic-es Swell the psalm of praise.
heaven a-bove, Shines in might vic-to-rious His e-ter-nal love.
cross our sky, Then, the veil up-lift-ing, Fa-ther, be Thou nigh.
pil-grim way, Go Thou still be-fore us To the end-less day. A-MEN.

Take Us on the Quest of Beauty   95

Eleanor B. Stock   PRAYER OF THE QUEST   Loeschorn

1. Take us on the Quest of Beau-ty, Po-et Seer of Gal-i-lee,
2. Take us on the Quest of Knowledge, Clear-est Think-er man has known!
3. Take us on the Quest of Serv-ice, King-ly Serv-ant of man's need,
4. All a-long our Quest's far pathways, Christ our Lead-er and our guide,

Mak-ing all our dreams cre-a-tive, Through their fel-low-ship with Thee.
Make our minds sin-cere and pa-tient, Sat-is-fied by Truth a-lone.
Let us work with Thee for oth-ers, An-y-where Thy pur-pose leads.
Make us con-scious of Thy presence, Walk-ing al-ways at our side.

The Prayer of the Quest was written especially to set forth the Christian Quest idea, and was first used at the Geneva Camp Conferences for Older Boys and Girls of the International Council of Religious Education.

Published by permission of the author. From *Singing Pathways*, edited by Mary S. Dickie and published by Powell and White, Cincinnati, Ohio.

96 He Leadeth Me

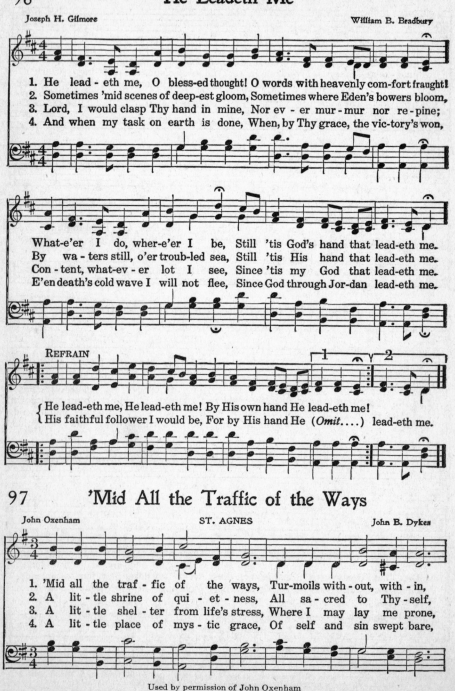

Joseph H. Gilmore

William B. Bradbury

1. He lead - eth me, O bless-ed thought! O words with heavenly com-fort fraught!
2. Sometimes 'mid scenes of deep-est gloom, Sometimes where Eden's bowers bloom,
3. Lord, I would clasp Thy hand in mine, Nor ev - er mur - mur nor re - pine;
4. And when my task on earth is done, When, by Thy grace, the vic-tory's won,

What-e'er I do, wher-e'er I be, Still 'tis God's hand that lead-eth me.
By wa - ters still, o'er troub-led sea, Still 'tis His hand that lead-eth me.
Con - tent, what-ev - er lot I see, Since 'tis my God that lead-eth me.
E'en death's cold wave I will not flee, Since God through Jor-dan lead-eth me.

REFRAIN

{ He lead-eth me, He lead-eth me! By His own hand He lead-eth me!
{ His faithful follower I would be, For by His hand He (*Omit....*) lead-eth me.

97 'Mid All the Traffic of the Ways

John Oxenham

ST. AGNES

John B. Dykes

1. 'Mid all the traf - fic of the ways, Tur-moils with - out, with - in,
2. A lit - tle shrine of qui - et - ness, All sa - cred to Thy - self,
3. A lit - tle shel - ter from life's stress, Where I may lay me prone,
4. A lit - tle place of mys - tic grace, Of self and sin swept bare,

Used by permission of John Oxenham

'Mid All the Traffic of the Ways

Make in my heart a qui - et place, And come and dwell there-in:
Where Thou shalt all my soul pos-sess, And I may find my - self:
And bare my soul in lone - li - ness, And know as I am known:
Where I may look up - on Thy face, And talk with Thee in prayer. A-MEN.

Dear Lord and Father of Mankind   98

John G. Whittier   ELTON   Frederick C. Maker

1. Dear Lord and Fa - ther of man - kind, For - give our fool - ish
2. In sim - ple trust like theirs who heard, Be - side the Syr - ian
3. Drop Thy still dews of qui - et - ness, Till all our striv - ings
4. Breathe through the heats of our de - sire Thy cool - ness and Thy

ways! Re - clothe us in our right - ful mind; In pur - er
sea The gra - cious call - ing of the Lord, Let us, like
cease; Take from our souls the strain and stress, And let our
balm; Let sense be dumb, let flesh re - tire; Speak through the

lives Thy serv - ice find, In deep - er rev - erence, praise.
them, with - out a word, Rise up and fol - low Thee.
or - dered lives con - fess The beau - ty of Thy peace.
earth-quake, wind, and fire, O still small voice of calm! A - MEN.

99 Father in Heaven, Hear Us Today

Charles G. Ames   SOUTHAMPTON   Anonymous

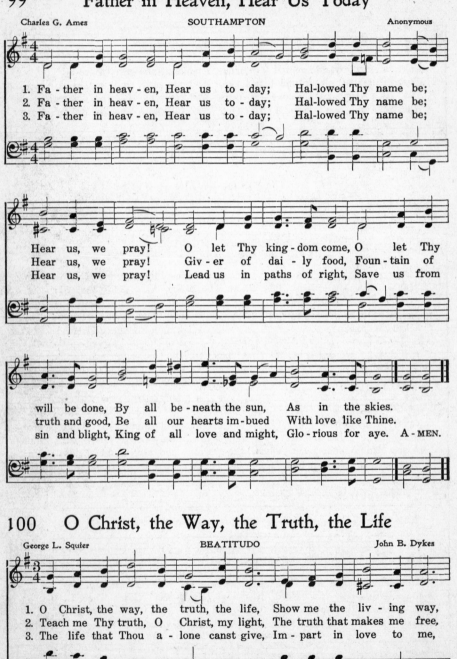

1. Fa - ther in heav - en, Hear us to - day; Hal-lowed Thy name be;
2. Fa - ther in heav - en, Hear us to - day; Hal-lowed Thy name be;
3. Fa - ther in heav - en, Hear us to - day; Hal-lowed Thy name be;

Hear us, we pray! O let Thy king - dom come, O let Thy
Hear us, we pray! Giv - er of dai - ly food, Foun - tain of
Hear us, we pray! Lead us in paths of right, Save us from

will be done, By all be - neath the sun, As in the skies.
truth and good, Be all our hearts im - bued With love like Thine.
sin and blight, King of all love and might, Glo - rious for aye. A - MEN.

100 O Christ, the Way, the Truth, the Life

George L. Squier   BEATITUDO   John B. Dykes

1. O Christ, the way, the truth, the life, Show me the liv - ing way,
2. Teach me Thy truth, O Christ, my light, The truth that makes me free,
3. The life that Thou a - lone canst give, Im - part in love to me,

O Christ, the Way, the Truth, the Life

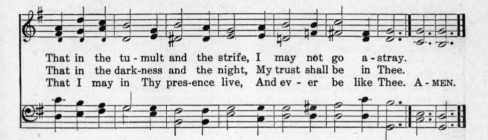

That in the tu-mult and the strife, I may not go a-stray.
That in the dark-ness and the night, My trust shall be in Thee.
That I may in Thy pres-ence live, And ev-er be like Thee. A-MEN.

Father in Heaven, Who Lovest All   101

Rudyard Kipling   SAXBY   Timothy R. Matthews

Land of our birth, we pledge to thee
Our love and toil in the years to be,
When we are grown and take our place
As men and women with our race.

1. Fa-ther in heaven, who lov-est all, O help Thy children when they call;
2. Teach us to bear the yoke in youth, With steadfastness and care-ful truth;
3. Teach us to rule our-selves al-way, Controlled and cleanly night and day;
4. Teach us to look in all our ends On Thee for Judge and not our friends;
5. Teach us the strength that cannot seek, By deed or thought, to hurt the weak;
6. Teach us de-light in sim-ple things, And mirth that has no bit-ter springs;

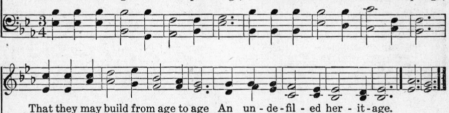

That they may build from age to age An un-de-fil-ed her-it-age.
That, in our time, Thy grace may give The truth whereby the nations live.
That we may bring, if need a-rise, No maimed or worthless sac-ri-fice.
That we, with Thee, may walk uncowed By fear or fa-vor of the crowd.
That, un-der Thee, we may possess Man's strength to comfort man's dis-tress.
For-give-ness free of e-vil done, And love to all men 'neath the sun. AMEN.

Land of our birth, our faith, our pride,
For whose dear sake our fathers died;
O Motherland, we pledge to thee
Head, heart, and hand through the years to be.

From *Puck of Pook's Hill* by Rudyard Kipling, printed by permission of Mrs. Kipling and Doubleday, Doran and Co. Inc., Publishers

102 What a Friend

Joseph Scriven

Charles C. Converse

1. What a Friend we have in Je - sus, All our sins and griefs to bear!
2. Have we tri - als and temp-ta - tions? Is there trou-ble an - y-where?
3. Are we weak and heav-y - la - den, Cum-bered with a load of care?

What a priv - i - lege to car - ry Ev - ery-thing to God in prayer!
We should nev - er be dis - cour-aged, Take it to the Lord in prayer.
Pre - cious Sav-iour, still our ref - uge— Take it to the Lord in prayer.

FINE

D.S.—All be-cause we do not car - ry Ev - ery-thing to God in prayer!
D.S.—Je - sus knows our ev - ery weak-ness, Take it to the Lord in prayer.
D.S.—In His arms He'll take and shield thee, Thou wilt find a sol - ace there.

D.S.

O what peace we oft - en for - feit, O what need-less pain we bear,
Can we find a friend so faith - ful Who will all our sor-rows share?
Do thy friends de-spise, for-sake thee? Take it to the Lord in prayer;

103 Lord, for Tomorrow and Its Needs

Sybil F. Partridge

BELLEVILLE

James Edmund Jones

1. Lord, for to - mor - row and its needs I do not pray; Keep
2. Let me both dil - i - gent - ly work And du - ly pray; Let
3. Let me be slow to do my will, Prompt to o - bey; Help
4. Let me no wrong nor i - dle word Un - think - ing say; Set
5. Lord, for to - mor - row and its needs, I do not pray; But

Music Copyright by James E. Jones

Lord, for Tomorrow and its Needs

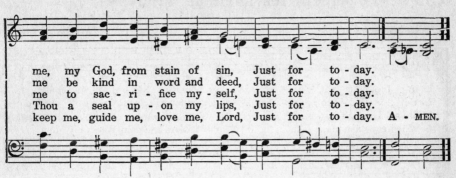

me,   my   God, from stain of   sin,   Just   for   to - day.
me   be   kind   in   word and   deed, Just   for   to - day.
me   to   sac - ri - fice my - self, Just for   to - day.
Thou a   seal up - on   my   lips, Just   for   to - day.
keep me, guide me, love me, Lord, Just for   to - day. A - MEN.

Father Almighty, Bless Us with Thy Blessing   104

Berwick Hymnal   INTEGER VITAE   Friedrich F. Flemming

1. Fa - ther Al - might - y, bless us with Thy bless - ing, An - swer in
2. Shep - herd of souls, who bring-est all who seek Thee To pas-tures
3. Fa - ther of mer - cy, from Thy watch and keep - ing   No place can

love Thy chil-dren's sup - pli - ca - tion; Hear Thou our prayer, the
green, be - side the peace-ful wa - ters; Ten - der - est guide, in
part, nor hour of time re - move us: Give us Thy good, and

spo - ken and un - spo - ken; Hear us, our Fa - ther.
ways of cheer - ful du - ty, Lead us, good Shep - herd.
save us from our e - vil, In - fi - nite Spir - it. A - MEN.

105 In the Hour of Trial

PENITENCE

James Montgomery

Spencer Lane

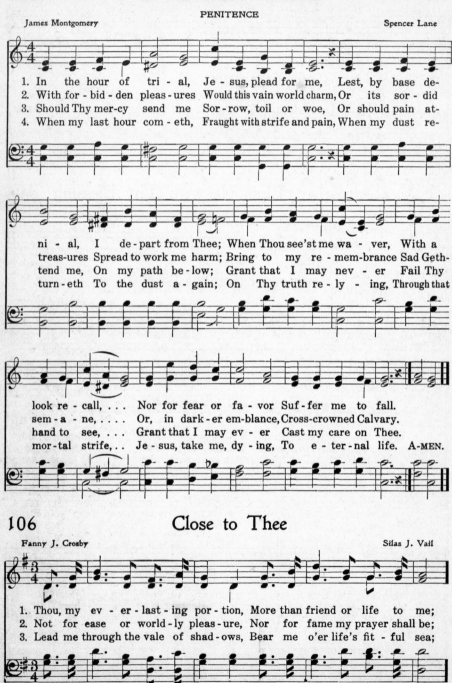

1. In the hour of tri - al, Je - sus, plead for me, Lest, by base de-
2. With for - bid - den pleas - ures Would this vain world charm, Or its sor - did
3. Should Thy mer-cy send me Sor - row, toil or woe, Or should pain at-
4. When my last hour com - eth, Fraught with strife and pain, When my dust re-

ni - al, I de - part from Thee; When Thou see'st me wa - ver, With a
treas-ures Spread to work me harm; Bring to my re - mem-brance Sad Geth-
tend me, On my path be - low; Grant that I may nev - er Fail Thy
turn - eth To the dust a - gain; On Thy truth re - ly - ing, Through that

look re - call, ... Nor for fear or fa - vor Suf - fer me to fall.
sem - a - ne, ... Or, in dark - er em-blance, Cross-crowned Calvary.
hand to see, ... Grant that I may ev - er Cast my care on Thee.
mor - tal strife, .. Je - sus, take me, dy - ing, To e - ter - nal life. A-MEN.

106 Close to Thee

Fanny J. Crosby

Silas J. Vail

1. Thou, my ev - er - last - ing por - tion, More than friend or life to me;
2. Not for ease or world - ly pleas - ure, Nor for fame my prayer shall be;
3. Lead me through the vale of shad - ows, Bear me o'er life's fit - ful sea;

Close to Thee

FINE

D.S.—All a-long my pil-grim jour-ney, Sav-iour, let me walk with Thee.
D.S.—Glad-ly will I toil and suf-fer, On-ly let me walk with Thee.
D.S.—Then the gate of life e-ter-nal May I en-ter, Lord, with Thee.

REFRAIN

D.S.

Close to Thee, close to Thee, Close to Thee, close to Thee;

More Love to Thee 107

Elizabeth Prentiss

William H. Doane

1. More love to Thee, O Christ, More love to Thee! Hear Thou the
2. Once earth-ly joy I craved, Sought peace and rest; Now Thee a-
3. Let sor-row do its work, Send grief and pain; Sweet are Thy
4. Then shall my lat-est breath Whis-per Thy praise; This be the

prayer I make On bend-ed knee; This is my ear-nest plea:
lone I seek, Give what is best; This all my prayer shall be:
mes-sen-gers, Sweet their re-frain, When they can sing with me:
part-ing cry My heart shall raise; This still its prayer shall be:

More love, O Christ, to Thee, More love to Thee, More love to Thee! A-MEN.

108 O Gracious Father of Mankind

Henry Hallam Tweedy ST. LEONARD Henry Hiles

1. O gra - cious Fa - ther of man-kind, Our   spir - its' un - seen Friend,
2. Thou hear - est these, the good and ill, Deep bur - ied in   each breast;
3. Our best is but Thy - self in us, Our   high - est thought Thy will;
4. Thou seek - est us   in love and truth More than our minds seek Thee;

High heav - en's Lord our hearts' dear Guest, To   Thee our prayers as - cend.
The   se - cret thought, the hid - den plan, Wrought out or un - ex - pressed.
To   hear Thy voice we   need but love, And lis - ten, and be   still.
Through o - pen gates Thy power flows in Like flood tides from the   sea.

Thou dost not wait till hu - man speech Thy gifts di - vine im - plore;
O cleanse our prayers from hu - man dross, At - tune our lives to Thee,
We would not bend Thy will to ours, But blend our wills with Thine;
No more we seek Thee from a - far, Nor ask Thee for a sign,

Our dreams, our aims, our work, our lives Are prayers Thou lov-est more.
Un - til we la - bor for those gifts We   ask on bend - ed knee.
Not beat with cries on heav-en's doors, But live Thy life di - vine.
Con - tent to pray in life and love And toil, till all are Thine. A-MEN.

Open My Eyes, That I May See

Clara H. Scott

Clara H. Scott

1. O - pen my eyes, that I may see Glimps-es of truth Thou hast for me;
2. O - pen my ears, that I may hear Voic - es of truth Thou send-est clear;
3. O - pen my mouth, and let me bear Glad - ly the warm truth ev - ery-where;

Place in my hands the won-der-ful key That shall un-clasp, and set me free.
And while the wave-notes fall on my ear, Ev-ery-thing false will dis - ap-pear.
O - pen my heart, and let me pre-pare Love with Thy chil-dren thus to share.

Si - lent - ly now I wait for Thee, Read - y, my God, Thy will to see;
Si - lent - ly now I wait for Thee, Read - y, my God, Thy will to see;
Si - lent - ly now I wait for Thee, Read - y, my God, Thy will to see;

O - pen my eyes, il - lu - mine me, Spir - it di - vine!
O - pen my ears, il - lu - mine me, Spir - it di - vine!
O - pen my heart, il - lu - mine me, Spir - it di - vine! A - MEN.

110 Father of Eternal Grace

MERCY

James Montgomery

Louis Gottschalk
Arr. by Edwin P. Parker

1. Fa - ther of e - ter - nal grace, Glo - ri - fy Thy - self in me;
2. Hap - py on - ly in Thy love, Poor, un - friend-ed, or un - known;
3. Hum - ble, ho - ly, all - re - signed To Thy will: Thy will be done!
4. Count-ing gain and glo - ry loss, May I tread the path He trod;

Meek - ly beam-ing in my face, May the world Thine im-age see.
Fix my thoughts on things a - bove, Stay my heart on Thee a - lone.
Give me, Lord, the per - fect mind Of Thy well - be - lov - ed Son.
Die with Je - sus on the cross, Rise with Him, to Thee, my God! A-MEN.

111 To Every Man There Openeth

DECISION

John Oxenham

George Henry Day

To ev - ery man there o-pen-eth a way, and

ways, and a way, . . . And the high soul climbs the high way, And the

To Every Man There Openeth

low soul gropes the low. . . . . And in be-tween, on the

mist - y flats, the rest drift to and fro. . . . But to ev-ery man there

o-pen-eth a high way and a low; . . . And ev - ery man de-

cid - eth the way his soul shall go. . . . .

112 Take Time to Be Holy

W. D. Longstaff

Geo. C. Stebbins

1. Take time to be ho-ly, Speak oft with thy Lord; A-bide in Him al-ways, And feed on His Word. Make friends of God's children; Help those who are weak; For-get-ting in noth-ing His bless-ing to seek.

2. Take time to be ho-ly, The world rush-es on; Much time spend in se-cret With Je-sus a-lone; By look-ing to Je-sus, Like Him thou shalt be; Thy friends in thy con-duct His like-ness shall see.

3. Take time to be ho-ly, Let Him be thy Guide, And run not be-fore Him, What-ev-er be-tide; In joy or in sor-row, Still fol-low thy Lord, And, look-ing to Je-sus, Still trust in His Word.

4. Take time to be ho-ly, Be calm in thy soul; Each thought and each mo-tive Be-neath His con-trol; Thus led by His Spir-it To foun-tains of love, Thou soon shalt be fit-ted For serv-ice a-bove. A-MEN.

113 God, Who Touchest Earth with Beauty

Mary S. Edgar

GENEVA

C. Harold Lowden

1. God, who touch-est earth with beau-ty, Make me love-ly too,
2. Like Thy springs and run-ning wa-ters, Make me crys-tal pure,
3. Like Thy danc-ing waves in sun-light, Make me glad and free,
4. Like the arch-ing of the heav-ens, Lift my thoughts a-bove,
5. God, who touch-est earth with beau-ty, Make me love-ly too,

God, Who Touchest Earth with Beauty

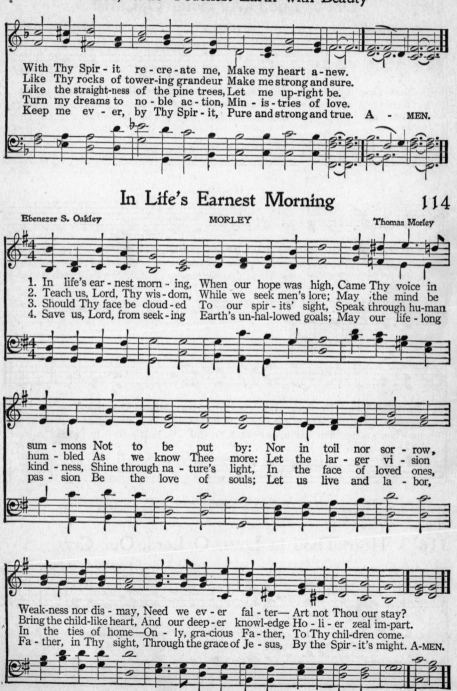

With Thy Spir - it re - cre - ate me, Make my heart a - new.
Like Thy rocks of tower-ing grandeur Make me strong and sure.
Like the straight-ness of the pine trees, Let me up-right be.
Turn my dreams to no - ble ac - tion, Min - is - tries of love.
Keep me ev - er, by Thy Spir - it, Pure and strong and true. A - MEN.

In Life's Earnest Morning   114

Ebenezer S. Oakley   MORLEY   Thomas Morley

1. In life's ear - nest morn - ing, When our hope was high, Came Thy voice in
2. Teach us, Lord, Thy wis - dom, While we seek men's lore; May the mind be
3. Should Thy face be cloud - ed To our spir - its' sight, Speak through hu - man
4. Save us, Lord, from seek - ing Earth's un-hal-lowed goals; May our life - long

sum - mons Not to be put by: Nor in toil nor sor - row,
hum - bled As we know Thee more: Let the lar - ger vi - sion
kind - ness, Shine through na - ture's light, In the face of loved ones,
pas - sion Be the love of souls; Let us live and la - bor,

Weak-ness nor dis - may, Need we ev - er fal - ter— Art not Thou our stay?
Bring the child-like heart, And our deep - er knowl-edge Ho - li - er zeal im-part.
In the ties of home—On - ly, gra-cious Fa - ther, To Thy chil-dren come.
Fa - ther, in Thy sight, Through the grace of Je - sus, By the Spir - it's might. A-MEN.

115 Draw Thou My Soul, O Christ

Lucy Larcom ST. EDMUND Arthur S. Sullivan

1. Draw Thou my soul, O Christ, Clos - er to Thine; Breathe in - to
2. Lead forth my soul, O Christ, One with Thine own, Joy - ful to
3. Not for my - self a - lone May my prayer be; Lift Thou Thy

ev - ery wish Thy will di - vine: Raised my low self a - bove, Won by Thy
fol - low Thee, Through paths unknown: In Thee my strength renew; Give me Thy
world, O Christ, Clos - er to Thee; Cleanse from its guilt and wrong, Teach it sal-

death-less love, Ev - er, O Christ, through mine Let Thy life shine.
work to do; Through me Thy truth be shown, Thy love made known.
va - tion's song, Till earth, as heaven, fu - fill God's ho - ly will. A-MEN.

Words used by permission of and by arrangement with Houghton Mifflin Co,
Music Copyright by Novello and Co., Ltd. Used by permission

116 Hear Thou in Love, O Lord, Our Cry

Felix Mendelssohn-Bartholdy

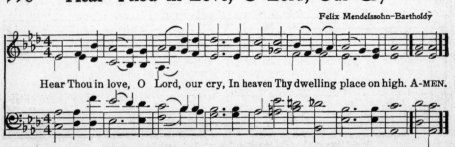

Hear Thou in love, O Lord, our cry, In heaven Thy dwelling place on high. A-MEN.

Temper My Spirit, O Lord

Jean Untermeyer

AGNI

Grace Wilbur Conant

Tem - per my spir-it, O Lord, Keep it long in the fire;

Make it one with the flame, let it share That up - reach-ing de-sire.

Grasp it, Thy-self, O my God; Swing it straight-er and high - er!

Tem-per my spir-it, O Lord, Tem-per my spir-it, O Lord. A - MEN.

Love Divine

Charles Wesley   BEECHER   John Zundel

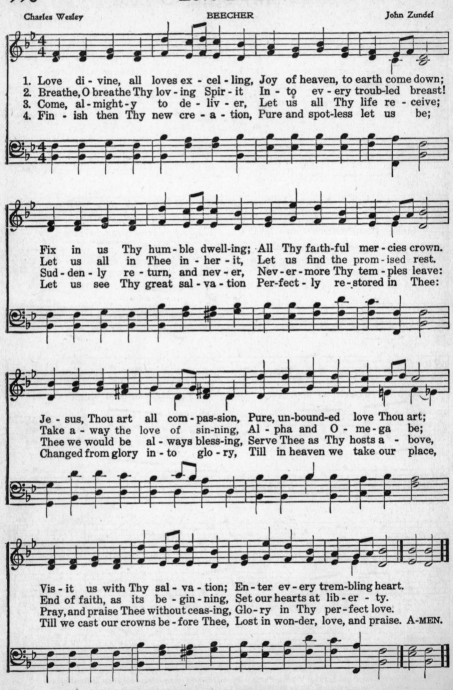

1. Love di - vine, all loves ex - cel - ling, Joy of heaven, to earth come down;
2. Breathe, O breathe Thy lov - ing Spir - it In - to ev - ery troub-led breast!
3. Come, al - might - y to de - liv - er, Let us all Thy life re - ceive;
4. Fin - ish then Thy new cre - a - tion, Pure and spot-less let us be;

Fix in us Thy hum - ble dwell-ing; All Thy faith-ful mer - cies crown.
Let us all in Thee in - her - it, Let us find the prom-ised rest.
Sud - den - ly re - turn, and nev - er, Nev - er - more Thy tem - ples leave:
Let us see Thy great sal - va - tion Per-fect - ly re-stored in Thee:

Je - sus, Thou art all com - pas-sion, Pure, un-bound-ed love Thou art;
Take a - way the love of sin-ning, Al - pha and O - me - ga be;
Thee we would be al - ways bless-ing, Serve Thee as Thy hosts a - bove,
Changed from glory in - to glo - ry, Till in heaven we take our place,

Vis - it us with Thy sal - va - tion; En - ter ev - ery trem-bling heart.
End of faith, as its be - gin - ning, Set our hearts at lib - er - ty.
Pray, and praise Thee without ceas-ing, Glo - ry in Thy per - fect love.
Till we cast our crowns be - fore Thee, Lost in won-der, love, and praise. A-MEN.

Are Ye Able, Said the Master

Earl Marlatt   BEACON HILL   Harry S. Mason

1. "Are ye a - ble," said the Mas - ter, "To be cru - ci - fied with Me?"
2. "Are ye a - ble" to re - mem - ber, When a thief lifts up his eyes,
3. "Are ye a - ble" when the shad - ows Close a - round you with the sod,
4. "Are ye a - ble," still the Mas - ter Whis - pers down e - ter - ni - ty,

"Yea," the stur - dy dream-ers an-swered, "To the death we fol - low Thee."
That his par-doned soul is wor - thy Of a place in Par - a - dise?
To be - lieve that spir - it tri - umphs, To com-mend your soul to God?
And he - ro - ic spir - its an - swer, Now, as then, in Gal - i - lee.

REFRAIN

"Lord, we are a - ble." Our spir - its are Thine. Re - mold them,

make us, Like Thee, di - vine. Thy guid - ing ra - diance A - bove us shall

be A bea - con to God, To faith and loy - al - ty. A-MEN.

Reprinted by permission of the author, Earl Marlatt, Boston University School of
Theology, 72 Mt. Vernon Street, Boston

120 March On, O Soul, with Strength

George T. Coster ARTHUR'S SEAT Arranged from John Goss

1. March on, O soul, with strength, Like those strong men of old Who
2. The sons of fa-thers we By whom our faith is taught To
3. March on, O soul, with strength, As strong the bat-tle rolls! 'Gainst

'gainst en-thron-ed wrong Stood con-fi-dent and bold; Who, thrust in
fear no ill, to fight The ho-ly fight they fought: He-ro-ic
lies and lusts and wrongs, Let cour-age rule our souls; In keen-est

prison or cast to flame, Still made their glo-ry in Thy name.
war-riors, ne'er from Christ By an-y lure or guile en-ticed.
strife, Lord, may we stand, Up-held and strengthened by Thy hand. A-MEN.

121 Strong Son of God, Immortal Love

Alfred Tennyson ST. CRISPIN George J. Elvey

1. Strong Son of God, im-mor-tal Love, Whom we, that have not seen Thy face,
2. Thou wilt not leave us in the dust: Thou mad-est man, he knows not why,
3. Thou seem-est hu-man and di-vine, The high-est, ho-liest man-hood, Thou;
4. Our lit-tle sys-tems have their day: They have their day and cease to be;
5. Let knowledge grow from more to more, But more of rev-erence in us dwell;

Strong Son of God, Immortal Love

By faith, and faith a-lone, em-brace, Be-liev-ing where we can-not prove;
He thinks he was not made to die: And Thou hast made him: Thou art just.
Our wills are ours, we know not how; Our wills are ours, to make them Thine.
They are but bro-ken lights of Thee, And Thou, O Lord, art more than they.
That mind and soul, ac-cord-ing well, May make one mu-sic as be-fore. A-MEN.

God of Grace and God of Glory   122

Harry Emerson Fosdick   REGENT SQUARE   Henry Smart

1. God of grace and God of glo-ry, On Thy peo-ple pour Thy pow'r;
2. Lo! the hosts of e-vil round us Scorn Thy Christ, as-sail His ways!
3. Cure Thy chil-dren's war-ring mad-ness, Bend our pride to Thy con-trol;
4. Set our feet on loft-y plac-es; Gird our lives that they may be
5. Save us from weak res-ig-na-tion To the e-vils we de-plore;

Crown Thine an-cient church's sto-ry; Bring her bud to glo-rious flower.
From the fears that long have bound us Free our hearts to faith and praise:
Shame our wan-ton, self-ish glad-ness, Rich in things and poor in soul.
Ar-mored with all Christ-like grac-es In the fight to set men free.
Let the search for Thy sal-va-tion Be our glo-ry ev-er-more.

Grant us wis-dom, Grant us cour-age, For the fac-ing of this hour.
Grant us wis-dom, Grant us cour-age, For the liv-ing of these days.
Grant us wis-dom, Grant us cour-age, Lest we miss Thy kingdom's goal.
Grant us wis-dom, Grant us cour-age, That we fail not man nor Thee!
Grant us wis-dom, Grant us cour-age, Serv-ing Thee whom we a-dore. A-MEN.

123 Fight the Good Fight with All Thy Might

John S. B. Monsell   PENTECOST   William Boyd

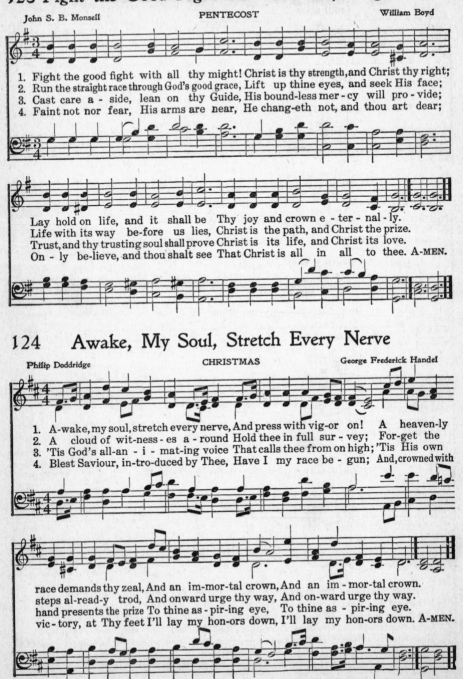

1. Fight the good fight with all thy might! Christ is thy strength, and Christ thy right;
2. Run the straight race through God's good grace, Lift up thine eyes, and seek His face;
3. Cast care a - side, lean on thy Guide, His bound-less mer - cy will pro - vide;
4. Faint not nor fear, His arms are near, He chang-eth not, and thou art dear;

Lay hold on life, and it shall be Thy joy and crown e - ter - nal - ly.
Life with its way be-fore us lies, Christ is the path, and Christ the prize.
Trust, and thy trusting soul shall prove Christ is its life, and Christ its love.
On - ly be-lieve, and thou shalt see That Christ is all in all to thee. A-MEN.

124   Awake, My Soul, Stretch Every Nerve

Philip Doddridge   CHRISTMAS   George Frederick Handel

1. A-wake, my soul, stretch every nerve, And press with vig-or on! A heaven-ly
2. A cloud of wit-ness-es a - round Hold thee in full sur - vey; For-get the
3. 'Tis God's all-an - i - mat-ing voice That calls thee from on high; 'Tis His own
4. Blest Saviour, in-tro-duced by Thee, Have I my race be - gun; And, crowned with

race demands thy zeal, And an im-mor-tal crown, And an im-mor-tal crown.
steps al-read-y trod, And onward urge thy way, And on-ward urge thy way.
hand presents the prize To thine as-pir-ing eye, To thine as-pir-ing eye.
vic-tory, at Thy feet I'll lay my hon-ors down, I'll lay my hon-ors down. A-MEN.

Be Strong! We Are Not Here to Play 125

FORTITUDE

Maltbie D. Babcock

David S. Smith

1. Be strong! We are not here to play, to dream, to drift: We have hard work to do and loads to lift; Shun not the strug-gle: face it— 'tis God's gift. Be strong, ... be strong! .. Be strong, ... be strong! ..

2. Be strong! Say not the days are e - vil— who's to blame? And fold the hands and ac - qui - esce— O shame! Stand up, speak out, and brave - ly, in God's Name, Be strong, ... be strong! ..

3. Be strong! It mat - ters not how deep en - trenched the wrong, How hard the bat - tle goes, the day, how long; Faint not, fight on! To - mor - row comes the song. Be strong, ... be strong! .. A - MEN.

126 Who Is on the Lord's Side

ARMAGEDDON

Frances R. Havergal

Arr. by John Goss

1. Who is on the Lord's side? Who will serve the King? Who will be His
2. Not for weight of glo - ry, Not for crown and palm, En - ter we the
3. Je - sus, Thou hast bought us, Not with gold or gem, But with Thine own
4. Fierce may be the con - flict, Strong may be the foe, But the King's own

help - ers, Oth - er lives to bring? Who will leave the world's side?
ar - my, Raise the war - rior psalm; But for love that claim - eth
life - blood, For Thy di - a - dem. With Thy bless - ing fill - ing
ar - my None can o - ver - throw. Round His stand-ard rang - ing

Who will face the foe? Who is on the Lord's side? Who for
Lives for whom He died; He whom Je - sus nam - eth Must be
Each who comes to Thee, Thou hast made us will - ing, Thou hast
Vic - tory is se - cure; For His truth un-chang - ing Makes the

Him will go? By Thy call of mer - cy, By Thy grace di - vine,
on His side. By Thy love con - strain - ing, By Thy grace di - vine,
made us free. By Thy grand re - demp - tion, By Thy grace di - vine,
tri - umph sure. Joy - ful - ly en - list - ing By Thy grace di - vine,

We are on the Lord's side, Sav - iour, we are Thine. A - MEN.

A Mighty Fortress Is Our God

Martin Luther
Tr. by Frederick H. Hedge

EIN FESTE BURG

Martin Luther

1. A might-y for-tress is our God, A bul-wark nev-er fail - ing;
2. Did we in our own strength con-fide, Our striv-ing would be los - - ing;
3. And though this world, with dev-ils filled, Should threaten to un - do us;
4. That word a - bove all earth-ly powers, No thanks to them, a - bid - - eth;

Our Help - er He, a - mid the flood Of mor - tal ills pre - vail - ing.
Were not the right man on our side, The man of God's own choos - ing.
We will not fear, for God hath willed His truth to tri - umph through us.
The Spir - it and the gifts are ours Through Him who with us sid - eth.

For still our an-cient foe Doth seek to work us woe; His craft and power are
Dost ask who that may be? Christ Je - sus, it is He, Lord Sab - a - oth His
The Prince of darkness grim, We trem-ble not for him; His rage we can en-
Let goods and kin-dred go, This mor - tal life al - so; The bod - y they may

great; And, armed with cru-el hate, On earth is not his e - qual.
name, From age to age the same, And He must win the bat - tle.
dure, For lo, his doom is sure, One lit - tle word shall fell him.
kill; God's truth a - bid - eth still, His king-dom is for - ev - er. A - MEN.

128 Faith of Our Fathers!

ST. CATHERINE

Frederick W. Faber

Henri F. Hemy
Arr. by James G. Walton

1. Faith of our fa - thers! liv - ing still In spite of dun-geon, fire, and sword:
2. Faith of our fa - thers, faith and prayer Have kept our country brave and free,
3. Faith of our fa - thers, we will strive To win all na - tions un - to thee;
4. Faith of our fa - thers, we will love Both friend and foe in all our strife,

O how our hearts beat high with joy When-e'er we hear that glo-rious word!
And through the truth that comes from God, Her chil-dren have true lib - er - ty:
And through the truth that comes from God, Man-kind shall then in - deed be free:
And preach thee, too, as love knows how, By kind - ly word and vir - tuous life:

Faith of our fa-thers, ho - ly faith! We will be true to thee till death!
Faith of our fa-thers, ho - ly faith! We will be true to thee till death!
Faith of our fa-thers, ho - ly faith! We will be true to thee till death!
Faith of our fa-thers, ho - ly faith! We will be true to thee till death! A-MEN.

129 That Cause Can Neither Be Lost Nor Stayed

Christian Ostergaard
Tr. by J. A. Aaberg

Danish Folk Tune

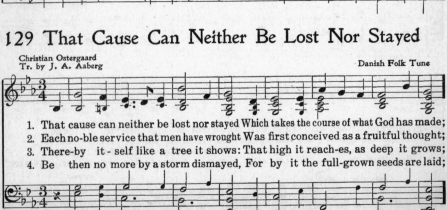

1. That cause can neither be lost nor stayed Which takes the course of what God has made;
2. Each no-ble service that men have wrought Was first conceived as a fruitful thought;
3. There-by it - self like a tree it shows: That high it reach-es, as deep it grows;
4. Be then no more by a storm dismayed, For by it the full-grown seeds are laid;

That Cause Can Neither Be Lost Nor Stayed

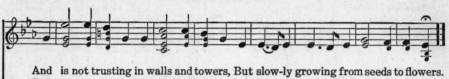

And is not trusting in walls and towers, But slow-ly growing from seeds to flowers.
Each worthy cause with a future glorious By qui - et growing becomes vic-to-rious.
And when the storms are its branches shaking, It deep-er root in the soil is tak-ing.
And though the tree by its might it shatters, What then, if thousands of seeds it scatters!

My Faith Looks Up to Thee 130

Ray Palmer   OLIVET   Lowell Mason

1. My   faith looks up   to Thee, Thou Lamb of   Cal - va - ry,
2. May   Thy rich grace im - part Strength to my faint - ing heart,
3. While life's dark maze   I tread, And griefs a - round me spread,
4. When ends life's tran - sient dream, When death's cold, sul - len stream

Sav - iour di - vine! Now hear me while I pray, Take all my
My   zeal in - spire; As   Thou hast died for me, O   may my
Be   Thou my Guide; Bid dark - ness turn to day, Wipe sor - row's
Shall o'er me roll; Blest Sav - iour, then, in love, Fear and dis-

guilt a - way, O let me from this day Be whol - ly Thine!
love to Thee Pure, warm, and changeless be, A   liv - ing fire!
tears a - way, Nor let me ev - er stray From Thee a - side.
trust re-move; O bear me safe a - bove, A   ran-somed soul! A-MEN.

131 My Faith It Is an Oaken Staff

MUSWELL HILL

Thomas T. Lynch

English Folksong
Arranged by Carey Bonner

Unison

1. My faith it is an oak-en staff, The trav-eler's well-loved aid;
2. I have a Guide, and in His steps When trav-elers lone have trod,
3. My faith it is an oak-en staff, O let me on it lean;

My faith it is a weap-on stout, The sol-dier's trust-ed blade. I'll
Wheth-er be-neath was flint-y rock Or yield-ing grass-y sod, They
My faith it is a trust-y sword, May false-hood find it keen, Thy

trav-el on and still be stirred By si-lent thought or so-cial word,
cared not, but with force un-spent, Un-moved by pain they on-ward went,
spir-it, Lord, to me im-part, O, make me what Thou ev-er art,

By all my per-ils un-de-terred, A sol-dier-pil-grim staid.
Un-stayed by pleas-ures till they bent Their zeal-ous course to God.
Of pa-tient and cour-a-geous heart, As all true saints have been. A-MEN.

I Love to Tell the Story

Katherine Hankey   William G. Fischer

1. I love to tell the sto - ry Of un - seen things a - bove, Of
2. I love to tell the sto - ry, More won-der - ful it seems Than
3. I love to tell the sto - ry, 'Tis pleas-ant to re - peat What
4. I love to tell the sto - ry, For those who know it best Seem

Je - sus and His glo - ry, Of Je - sus and His love. I love to
all the gold - en fan - cies Of all our gold - en dreams. I love to
seems, each time I tell it, More won - der - ful - ly sweet. I love to
hun - ger - ing and thirst - ing To hear it like the rest. And when, in

tell the sto - ry, Be - cause I know 'tis true; It sat - is - fies my
tell the sto - ry, It did so much for me; And that is just the
tell the sto - ry, For some have nev - er heard The mes - sage of sal -
scenes of glo - ry, I sing the new, new song, 'Twill be the old, old

CHORUS

long-ings As noth-ing else can do.
rea - son I tell it now to thee. I love to tell the sto - ry, 'Twill
va - tion From God's own Ho-ly Word.
sto - ry That I have loved so long.

be my theme in glo - ry To tell the old, old sto - ry Of Je - sus and His love.

133 God's Trumpet Wakes the Slumbering World

Samuel Longfellow   WARRIOR   Archibald MacDonald

1. God's trump-et wakes the slumbering world; Now, each man to his post.
2. He who, no an-ger on his tongue, Nor an-y i-dle boast,
3. He who is read-y for the cross, The cause de-spised loves most,

The red-cross ban-ner is un-furled; Who joins the glo-rious host?
Bears stead-fast wit-ness 'gainst the wrong, He joins the sa-cred host;
And shuns not pain or shame or loss, He joins the mar-tyr host.

He who, in feal-ty to the truth, And count-ing all the cost,
He who, with calm un-daunt-ed will, Ne'er counts the bat-tle lost,
God's trump-et wakes the slumbering world; Now, each man to his post;

Doth con-se-crate his gen-erous youth; He joins the no-ble host.
But, though de-feat-ed, bat-tles still, He joins the faith-ful host.
The red-cross ban-ner is un-furled; We join the glo-rious host. A-MEN.

How Firm a Foundation

PORTUGUESE HYMN

"K" in Rippon's Selection

J. F. Wade's Cantus Diversi

1. How firm a foun-da-tion, ye saints of the Lord, Is laid for your
2. "Fear not, I am with thee, O be not dis-mayed, For I am thy
3. "When through the deep waters I call thee to go, The riv-ers of
4. "When through fi-ery tri-als thy path-way shall lie, My grace all-suf-
5. "The soul that on Je-sus hath leaned for re-pose, I will not, I

faith in His ex-cel-lent Word! What more can He say than to
God, and will still give thee aid; I'll strength-en thee, help thee, and
sor-row shall not o-ver-flow, For I will be with thee, thy
fi-cient shall be thy sup-ply; The flame shall not hurt thee; I
will not de-sert to his foes; That soul, though all hell should en-

you He hath said, To you who for ref-uge to Je-sus have
cause thee to stand, Up-held by My right-eous, om-nip-o-tent
trou-bles to bless, And sanc-ti-fy to thee thy deep-est dis-
on-ly de-sign Thy dross to con-sume, and thy gold to re-
deav-or to shake, I'll nev-er, no nev-er, no nev-er for-

fled? To you who for ref-uge to Je-sus have fled?
hand, Up-held by My right-eous, om-nip-o-tent hand.
tress, And sanc-ti-fy to thee thy deep-est dis-tress.
fine, Thy dross to con-sume, and thy gold to re-fine.
sake! I'll nev-er, no nev-er, no nev-er for-sake!" A-MEN.

135 To the Knights in the Days of Old

Bryn Mawr Silver Bay
Prize Song, 1920

FOLLOW THE GLEAM

Sallie Hume Douglas

Unison

1. To the knights in the days of old, ... Keep-ing watch on the
2. And we who would serve the King . . . . And loy - al - ly

moun - tain heights, . . Came a vi - sion of Ho - ly Grail, . . .
Him o - bey, ... In the con - se-crate si - lence know . . . .

And a voice through the wait-ing night. . . . Fol - low, fol - - low,
That the chal-lenge still holds to - day. . . . . Fol - low, fol - - low,

fol - low the gleam, Ban-ners un-furled o'er all the world, Fol-low, fol-
fol - low the gleam, Standards of worth o'er all the earth, Fol-low, fol-

low, fol - low the gleam Of the chal - ice that is the Grail. . . . .
low, fol - low the gleam Of the light that shall bring the dawn. . . . .

Make Me a Captive, Lord

LEOMINSTER

George Matheson

George W. Martin
Arr. by Arthur S. Sullivan

1. Make me a cap-tive, Lord, And then I shall be free;
2. My heart is weak and poor Un-til it mas-ter find;
3. My power is faint and low Till I have learned to serve;
4. My will is not my own Till Thou hast made it Thine;

Force me to ren-der up my sword, And I shall con-queror be.
It has no spring of ac-tion sure—It va-ries with the wind.
It wants the need-ed fire to glow, It wants the breeze to nerve;
If it would reach a mon-arch's throne It must its crown re-sign;

I sink in life's a-larms When by my-self I stand;
It can-not free-ly move Till Thou hast wrought its chain;
It can-not drive the world, Un-til it-self be driven;
It on-ly stands un-bent, A-mid the clash-ing strife,

Im-pris-on me with-in Thine arms, And strong shall be my hand.
En-slave it with Thy match-less love, And death-less it shall reign.
Its flag can on-ly be un-furled When Thou shalt breathe from heaven.
When on Thy bos-om it has leant And found in Thee its life. A-MEN.

137 Stand Up for Jesus

George Duffield

WEBB

George J. Webb

1. Stand up, stand up for Je-sus, Ye sol-diers of the cross, Lift high His
2. Stand up, stand up for Je-sus, The trump-et call o-bey; Forth to the
3. Stand up, stand up for Je-sus, Stand in His strength a-lone; The arm of
4. Stand up, stand up for Je-sus, The strife will not be long; This day the

roy - al ban-ner, It must not suf-fer loss; From vic-tory un-to vic-tory, His
might-y con-flict, In this His glorious day. "Ye that are men, now serve Him," A-
flesh will fail you—Ye dare not trust your own; Put on the gos-pel ar-mor, Each
noise of bat-tle, The next, the vic-tor's song; To him that o-ver-com-eth, A

ar - my shall He lead, Till ev-ery foe is vanquished And Christ is Lord in-deed.
gainst unnumbered foes; Let courage rise with dan-ger, And strength to strength oppose.
piece put on with prayer; Where du-ty calls, or dan-ger, Be nev-er want-ing there.
crown of life shall be; He with the King of glo-ry Shall reign e-ter-nal-ly. A-MEN.

138 Lord, Speak to Me

Frances R. Havergal

CANONBURY

Robert Schumann

1. Lord, speak to me, that I may speak In liv-ing ech-oes of Thy tone;
2. O teach me, Lord, that I may teach The pre-cious things Thou dost im-part;
3. O fill me with Thy full-ness, Lord, Un-til my ver-y heart o'er-flow
4. O use me, Lord, use e-ven me, Just as Thou wilt, and when, and where;

Lord, Speak to Me

As Thou hast sought, so let me seek Thy err-ing chil-dren lost and lone.
And wing my words, that they may reach The hid-den depths of many a heart.
In kindling thought and glow-ing word, Thy love to tell, Thy praise to show.
Un - til Thy bless-ed face I see, Thy rest, Thy joy, Thy glo - ry share. AMEN.

I Would Be True   139

Howard Arnold Walter   PEEK   Joseph Yates Peek

1. I would be true, for there are those who trust me; I would be
2. I would be friend of all— the foe, the friend-less; I would be

pure, for there are those who care; I would be strong, for there is
giv - ing, and for - get the gift; I would be hum - ble, for I

much to suf - fer; I would be brave, for there is much to
know my weak - ness; I would look up, and laugh, and love, and

dare; I would be brave, for there is much to dare.
lift; I would look up, and laugh, and love, and lift. A-MEN.

140 Now in the Days of Youth

DIADEMATA

Walter J. Mathams

George J. Elvey

1. Now in the days of youth, When life flows fresh and free,
2. Teach us wher-e'er we live, To act as in Thy sight,
3. Teach us to love the true, The beau - ti - ful and pure,
4. Spir - it of Christ, do Thou Our first bright days in - spire

Thou Lord of all our hearts and lives, We give our-selves to Thee;
And do what Thou wouldst have us do With ra - di - ant de - light;
And let us not for one short hour An e - vil thought en - dure;
That we may live the life of love And loft - i - est de - sire;

Our fer - vent gift re - ceive, And fit us to ful - fill,
Not choos - ing what is great, Nor spurn - ing what is small,
But give us grace to stand De - cid - ed, brave and strong,
And be by Thee pre - pared For larg - er years to come,

Through all our days, in all our ways, Our heaven-ly Fa-ther's will.
But take as from Thy hands our tasks, And glo - ri - fy them all.
The lov - ers of all ho - ly things, The foes of all things wrong.
And for the life in - ef - fa - ble With-in the Fa-ther's home. A-MEN.

Jesus, Thy Boundless Love

Paul Gerhardt
Tr. by John Wesley
Altered and revised

STELLA

Old English Melody

1. Je - sus, Thy bound - less love to me No thought can
2. O grant that noth - ing in my soul May dwell, but
3. O Love, how gra - cious is Thy way! All fear be-

reach, no tongue de - clare; O knit my thank - ful heart to
Thy pure love a - lone; O may Thy love pos - sess me
fore Thy pres - ence flies; Care, an - guish, sor - row, melt a-

Thee, And reign with - out a ri - val there! Thine whol - ly,
whole, My joy, my treas - ure, and my crown! All cold - ness
way, Wher - e'er Thy heal - ing beams a - rise. O Je - sus,

Thine a - lone, I'd live, My - self to Thee en - tire - ly give.
from my heart re - move; May ev - ery act, word, thought, be love.
noth - ing may I see, Noth - ing de - sire, or seek, but Thee. A-MEN.

142 Saviour, Thy Dying Love

Sylvanus D. Phelps

SOMETHING FOR THEE

Robert Lowry

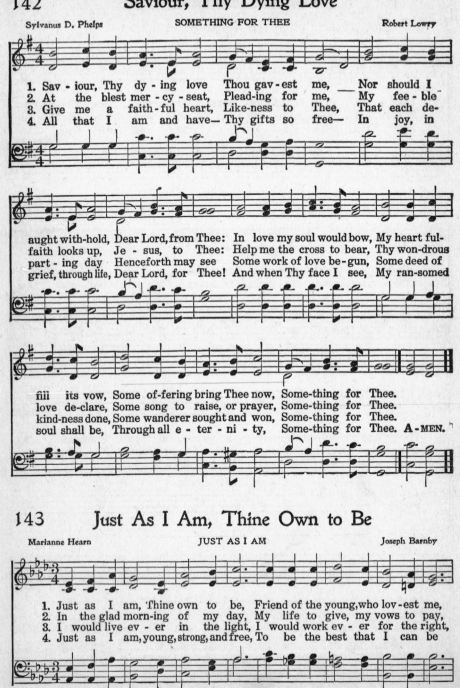

1. Sav - iour, Thy dy - ing love Thou gav - est me, __ Nor should I
2. At the blest mer - cy - seat, Plead-ing for me, My fee - ble
3. Give me a faith - ful heart, Like-ness to Thee, That each de-
4. All that I am and have— Thy gifts so free— In joy, in

aught with-hold, Dear Lord, from Thee: In love my soul would bow, My heart ful-
faith looks up, Je - sus, to Thee: Help me the cross to bear, Thy won-drous
part - ing day Henceforth may see Some work of love be-gun, Some deed of
grief, through life, Dear Lord, for Thee! And when Thy face I see, My ran-somed

fill its vow, Some of-fering bring Thee now, Some-thing for Thee.
love de-clare, Some song to raise, or prayer, Some-thing for Thee.
kind-ness done, Some wanderer sought and won, Some-thing for Thee.
soul shall be, Through all e - ter - ni - ty, Some-thing for Thee. A - MEN.

143 Just As I Am, Thine Own to Be

Marianne Hearn

JUST AS I AM

Joseph Barnby

1. Just as I am, Thine own to be, Friend of the young, who lov - est me,
2. In the glad morn-ing of my day, My life to give, my vows to pay,
3. I would live ev - er in the light, I would work ev - er for the right,
4. Just as I am, young, strong, and free, To be the best that I can be

Just As I Am, Thine Own to Be

To con-se-crate my-self to Thee, O Je-sus Christ, I come.
With no re-serve and no de-lay, With all my heart I come.
I would serve Thee with all my might; There-fore to Thee I come.
For truth, and right-eous-ness and Thee, Lord of my life, I come. A-MEN.

We Would Be Building 144

FINLANDIA

Purd E. Deitz

Jean Sibelius
Arr. for "The Hymnal"

1. We would be build-ing; tem-ples still un-done .... O'er crumbling walls their
2. Teach us to build; up-on the sol-id rock .... We set the dream that
3. O keep us build-ing, Mas-ter; may our hands ... Ne'er fal-ter when the

cross-es scarce-ly lift; Wait-ing till love can raise the bro-ken stone, ...
hard-ens in-to deed, Ribbed with the steel that time and change doth mock,
dream is in our hearts, When to our ears there come di-vine com-mands ...

And hearts cre-a-tive bridge the hu-man rift;.. We would be build-ing,
Th' un-fail-ing pur-pose of our no-blest creed; Teach us to build; O
And all the pride of sin-ful will de-parts; We build with Thee, O

Mas-ter, let Thy plan ... Re-veal the life that God would give to man.
Mas-ter, lend us sight ... To see the tow-ers gleam-ing in the light.
grant en-dur-ing worth .. Un-til the heavenly Kingdom comes on earth. A-MEN.

145 Pass On the Torch

TORCHBEARERS

Allen Eastman Cross

Nathaniel Irving Hyatt

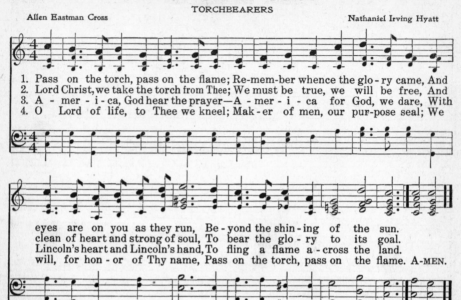

1. Pass on the torch, pass on the flame; Re-mem-ber whence the glo-ry came, And
2. Lord Christ, we take the torch from Thee; We must be true, we will be free, And
3. A - mer - i - ca, God hear the prayer—A - mer - i - ca for God, we dare, With
4. O Lord of life, to Thee we kneel; Mak-er of men, our pur-pose seal; We

eyes are on you as they run, Be-yond the shin-ing of the sun.
clean of heart and strong of soul, To bear the glo-ry to its goal.
Lincoln's heart and Lincoln's hand, To fling a flame a-cross the land.
will, for hon-or of Thy name, Pass on the torch, pass on the flame. A-MEN.

Words Copyright by Allen Eastman Cross
Music Copyright by D. Appleton Century Co. Used by permission

146 Jesus, I Live to Thee

LAKE ENON

Henry Harbaugh

Isaac B. Woodbury

Not too fast

1. Je - sus, I live to Thee, The love - li - est and best;
2. Je - sus, I die to Thee, When-ev - er death shall come;
3. Wheth-er to live or die, I know not which is best;
4. Liv - ing or dy - ing, Lord, I ask but to be Thine;

My life in Thee, Thy life in me, In Thy blest love I rest.
To die in Thee is life to me, In my e - ter-nal home.
To live in Thee is bliss to me, To die is end-less rest.
My life in Thee, Thy life in me, Makes heaven for-ev-er mine. A-MEN.

Give of Your Best to the Master

H. B. G.

Mrs. Charles Barnard

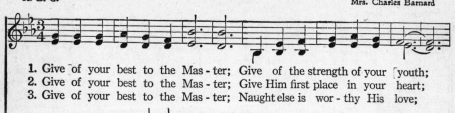

1. Give of your best to the Mas - ter; Give of the strength of your youth;
2. Give of your best to the Mas - ter; Give Him first place in your heart;
3. Give of your best to the Mas - ter; Naught else is wor - thy His love;

REF.—*Give of your best to the Mas - ter; Give of the strength of your youth;*

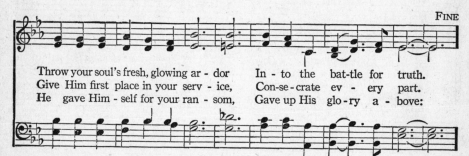

FINE

Throw your soul's fresh, glowing ar - dor In - to the bat - tle for truth.
Give Him first place in your serv - ice, Con - se - crate ev - ery part.
He gave Him - self for your ran - som, Gave up His glo - ry a - bove:

Clad in sal - va - tion's full ar - mor, Join in the bat - tle for truth.

Je - sus has set the ex - am - ple; Daunt-less was He, young and brave;
Give, and to you shall be giv - en; God His be - lov - ed Son gave;
Laid down His life with-out mur - mur, You from sin's ru - in to save;

rall.   D. C.

Give Him your loy - al de - vo - tion, Give Him the best that you have.
Grate - ful - ly seek - ing to serve Him, Give Him the best that you have.
Give Him your heart's ad - o - ra - tion, Give Him the best that you have.

O Jesus, Thou Art Standing

ST. HILDA

William W. How

Justin H. Knecht
Edward Husband

1. O Je-sus, Thou art standing Out-side the fast-closed door, In low-ly pa-tience
2. O Je-sus, Thou art knocking; And lo! that hand is scarred, And thorns Thy brow en-
3. O Je-sus, Thou art pleading In ac-cents meek and low, "I died for you, My

wait-ing To pass the thresh-old o'er: Shame on us, Christian brothers, His Name and
cir-cle, And tears Thy face have marred: O love that passeth knowledge, So pa-tient-
chil-dren, And will ye treat Me so?" O Lord, with shame and sorrow We o-pen

sign who bear, O shame, thrice shame up-on us, To keep Him standing there!
ly to wait! O sin that hath no e-qual, So fast to bar the gate!
now the door; Dear Saviour, en-ter, en-ter, And leave us nev-er-more! A-MEN.

149 The King of Love My Shepherd Is

DOMINUS REGIT ME

From Psalm 23
Henry W. Baker

John B. Dykes

1. The King of love my Shep-herd is, Whose good-ness fail-eth nev-er;
2. Where streams of liv-ing wa-ter flow My ran-somed soul He lead-eth,
3. In death's dark vale I fear no ill With Thee, dear Lord, be-side me;
4. And so through all the length of days, Thy good-ness fail-eth nev-er:

The King of Love My Shepherd Is

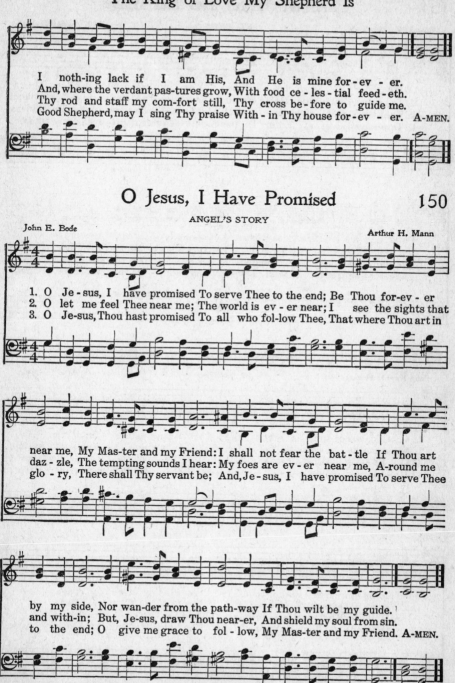

I noth-ing lack if I am His, And He is mine for-ev-er.
And, where the verdant pas-tures grow, With food ce-les-tial feed-eth.
Thy rod and staff my com-fort still, Thy cross be-fore to guide me.
Good Shepherd, may I sing Thy praise With-in Thy house for-ev-er. A-MEN.

O Jesus, I Have Promised

150

ANGEL'S STORY

John E. Bode

Arthur H. Mann

1. O Je-sus, I have promised To serve Thee to the end; Be Thou for-ev-er
2. O let me feel Thee near me; The world is ev-er near; I see the sights that
3. O Je-sus, Thou hast promised To all who fol-low Thee, That where Thou art in

near me, My Mas-ter and my Friend: I shall not fear the bat-tle If Thou art
daz-zle, The tempting sounds I hear: My foes are ev-er near me, A-round me
glo-ry, There shall Thy servant be; And, Je-sus, I have promised To serve Thee

by my side, Nor wan-der from the path-way If Thou wilt be my guide.
and with-in; But, Je-sus, draw Thou near-er, And shield my soul from sin.
to the end; O give me grace to fol-low, My Mas-ter and my Friend. A-MEN.

151 Take My Life, and Let It Be

Frances R. Havergal
ST. BEES
John Bacchus Dykes

1. Take my life, and let it be Con-se-crat-ed, Lord, to Thee;
2. Take my hands, and let them move At the im-pulse of Thy love;
3. Take my will, and make it Thine; It shall be no lon-ger mine;
4. Take my love; my Lord, I pour At Thy feet its treas-ure-store;

Take my mo-ments and my days, Let them flow in cease-less praise.
Take my feet, and let them be Swift and beau-ti-ful for Thee.
Take my heart; it is Thine own, It shall be Thy roy-al throne.
Take my-self, and I will be Ev-er, on-ly, all for Thee. A-MEN.

152 O God, Whose Smile Is in the Sky

John Haynes Holmes
ST. AGNES
John B. Dykes

1. O God, whose smile is in the sky, Whose path is in the sea,
2. We come as those with toil far spent Who crave Thy rest and peace,
3. O Fa-ther, soothe all troub-led thoughts, Dis-pel all i-dle fear,
4. Un-til, as shine up-on the sea The si-lent stars a-bove,

Once more from earth's tu-mul-tuous strife, We glad-ly turn to Thee.
And from the care and fret of life Would find in Thee re-lease.
Purge Thou each heart of se-cret sin, And ban-ish ev-ery care;
There shines up-on our trust-ing souls The light of Thine own love. A-MEN.

Words used by permission of John H. Holmes

Be Thou My Vision

Ancient Irish. Arranged by
Mary Byrne and Eleanor Hull

PENITENTIA

Edward Dearle

1. Be Thou my vi - sion, O Lord of my heart;
2. Be Thou my wis - dom, O Thou my true Word;
3. Be Thou my bat - tle - shield, sword for the fight;
4. Rich - es I heed not, nor man's emp - ty praise,

Naught be all else to me, save that Thou art,—
I ev - er with Thee, and Thou with me, Lord;
Be Thou my dig - ni - ty, Thou my de - light,
Thou mine in - her - it - ance, now and al - ways;

Thou my best thought, by day or by night,
Thou my great Fa - ther, I Thy true son;
Thou my soul's shel - ter, Thou my high tower:
Thou and Thou on - ly, first in my heart,

Wak - ing or sleep - ing, Thy pres - ence my light.
Thou in me dwell - ing, and I with Thee one.
Raise Thou me heav - en - ward, power of my power.
High King of heav - en, my treas - ure Thou art. A - MEN.

154 Living for Jesus

Thomas O. Chisholm

C. Harold Lowden

Not fast

1. Liv-ing for Je-sus a life that is true, Striv-ing to please Him in
2. Liv-ing for Je-sus who died in my place, Bear-ing on Cal-vary my
3. Liv-ing for Je-sus wher-ev-er I am, Do-ing each du-ty in
4. Liv-ing for Je-sus through earth's lit-tle while, My dear-est treas-ure, the

all that I do; Yield-ing al - le-giance, glad-heart-ed and free,
sin and dis-grace; Such love con-strains me to an-swer His call,
His ho-ly name; Will-ing to suf-fer af-flic-tion and loss,
light of His smile; Seek-ing the lost ones He died to re-deem,

CHORUS Unison. Slower

This is the path-way of bless-ing for me.
Fol-low His lead-ing and give Him my all. O Je-sus, Lord and
Deem-ing each tri-al a part of my cross.
Bring-ing the wea-ry to find rest in Him.

Sav-iour, I give my-self to Thee, For Thou, in Thy a-tone-ment, Didst

give Thy-self for me; I own no oth-er Mas-ter, My heart shall be Thy

*Melody in lower notes. A two-part effect may be had by having the men sing the melody, the women taking the middle notes.

Keep Thyself Pure! Christ's Soldier

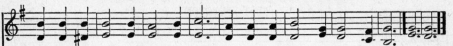

Thy Cap-tain speaks; His word o-bey; So shall thy strength be as thy day.
His feet shall stand where saints have trod, He with rapt eyes shall see his God.
Then hear Him speaking from the skies; And vic-tor o'er temp-ta-tion rise.
Our bod-ies are Thy tem-ple, Lord; Be Thou in thought and act a-dored. A-MEN.

The Body, Lord, Is Ours to Keep   158

Eleanor B. Stock   DOLUT   Sebastian W. Meyer

1. The bod-y, Lord, is ours to keep In glowing health and strength for Thee,
2. The mind, O Lord, is ours to keep In clean-li-ness and pu-ri-ty,
3. The soul, O Lord, is ours to keep In close com-pan-ion-ship with Thee,

That through its life Thy life may live, Thy will move strong and swift and free;
That ev-ery thought and word and deed May own it-self a-kin to Thee;
That soul is bod-y, mind and heart, And these are but a u-ni-ty;

My bod-y, Lord, is Thine to keep, Strong and swift and free.
My mind, O Lord, is Thine to keep, Clean and pure and free.
My soul, O Lord, is Thine to keep In com-rade-ship with Thee. A-MEN.

Published by permission of the author. From *Singing Pathways*, edited by Mary S. Dickie and published by Powell and White, Cincinnati, Ohio

159 God of Our Youth, to Whom We Yield

LEST WE FORGET

William Byron Forbush, Altered

George F. Blanchard

1. God of our youth, to whom we yield The trib - ute of our ea - ger praise, Up - on the well - con - test - ed field, And 'mid the glo - ry of these days, God of our youth, be with us yet, Lest we for - get, lest we for - get.

2. Stur - dy of limb, with bound - ing health, Ea - ger to play the he - ro's part, Grant to us each that great - er wealth, An un - de - filed and loy - al heart, God of our youth, be Thou our might, To do the right, to do the right.

3. When from the field of mim - ic strife, Of strength with strength, and speed with speed, We face the stern - er fights of life, As then our strength in time of need, God of our youth, in spire us still, To do Thy will, to do Thy will. A - MEN.

Music Copyright by Reid Brothers, Ltd.

These Things Shall Be,—A Loftier Race 160

John A. Symonds   TRURO   Charles Burney

1. These things shall be,—a loft-ier race Than e'er the world hath known shall rise
2. They shall be gen-tle, brave, and strong To spill no drop of blood, but dare
3. Na - tion with na-tion, land with land, Un-armed shall live as com-rades free;
4. New arts shall bloom of loft-ier mould, And might-ier mu - sic thrill the skies,

With flame of freedom in their souls, And light of knowl-edge in their eyes.
All that may plant man's lord-ship firm On earth, and fire, and sea, and air.
In ev-ery heart and brain shall throb The pulse of one fra - ter-ni - ty.
And ev-ery life shall be a song, When all the earth is par-a-dise. AMEN.

When Thy Heart with Joy O'erflowing 161

Theodore Chickering Williams   BULLINGER   Ethelbert W. Bullinger

1. When thy heart with joy o'er-flow-ing, Sings a thank-ful prayer,
2. When the har - vest sheaves in-gath-ered, Fill thy barns with store,
3. If thy soul, with power up-lift-ed, Yearn for glo-rious deed,
4. Share with him thy bread of bless-ing, Sor-row's bur-den share:

In thy joy, O let thy broth-er With thee share.
To thy God and to thy broth-er Give the more.
Give thy strength to serve thy broth-er In his need.
When thy heart en-folds a broth-er God is there. A-MEN.

From *The Hymn and Tune Book.* Copyright The Beacon Press, Inc. Used by permission

162 O Brother Man, Fold to Thy Heart

John Greenleaf Whittier   LANHERNE   Henry Hayman

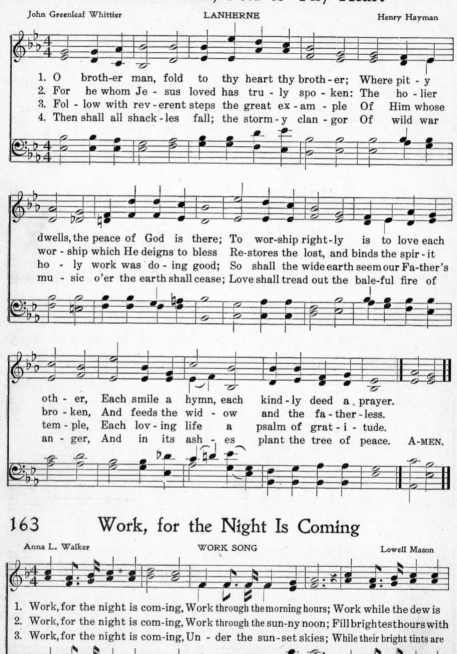

1. O broth-er man, fold to thy heart thy broth-er; Where pit - y
2. For he whom Je - sus loved has tru - ly spo - ken: The ho - lier
3. Fol - low with rev - erent steps the great ex - am - ple Of Him whose
4. Then shall all shack - les fall; the storm - y clan - gor Of wild war

dwells, the peace of God is there; To wor-ship right-ly is to love each
wor - ship which He deigns to bless Re-stores the lost, and binds the spir - it
ho - ly work was do - ing good; So shall the wide earth seem our Fa-ther's
mu - sic o'er the earth shall cease; Love shall tread out the bale-ful fire of

oth - er, Each smile a hymn, each kind - ly deed a prayer.
bro - ken, And feeds the wid - ow and the fa - ther - less.
tem - ple, Each lov - ing life a psalm of grat - i - tude.
an - ger, And in its ash - es plant the tree of peace. A-MEN.

163 Work, for the Night Is Coming

Anna L. Walker   WORK SONG   Lowell Mason

1. Work, for the night is com-ing, Work through the morning hours; Work while the dew is
2. Work, for the night is com-ing, Work through the sun-ny noon; Fill brightest hours with
3. Work, for the night is com-ing, Un - der the sun-set skies; While their bright tints are

Work, for the Night Is Coming

spark-ling; Work 'mid springing flowers. Work when the day grows bright-er, Work in the
la - bor, Rest comes sure and soon. Give ev - ery fly - ing min - ute Something to
glow- ing, Work, for day-light flies. Work till the last beam fad- eth, Fad - eth to

glow - ing sun; Work, for the night is com - ing, When man's work is done.
keep in store; Work, for the night is com - ing, When man works no more.
shine no more; Work while the night is darkening, When man's work is o'er. A-MEN.

O Son of Man, Thou Madest Known 164

Milton S. Littlefield   BROOKFIELD   Thomas B. Southgate

1. O Son of Man, Thou mad-est known, Through qui-et work in shop and home,
2. O Work-man true, may we ful - fil In dai - ly life Thy Fa - ther's will;
3. Thou Mas-ter Work-man, grant us grace, The chal-lenge of our tasks to face;
4. And thus we pray in deed and word, Thy king-dom come on earth, O Lord.

The sa-cred-ness of com-mon things, The chance of life that each day brings.
In du-ty's call, Thy call we hear To full - er life, thro' work sin-cere.
By loy - al scorn of sec-ond best, By ef - fort true, to meet each test.
In work that gives ef-fect to prayer Thy pur-pose for Thy world we share. A- MEN.

165 God Send Us Men Whose Aim 'Twill Be

Frederick J. Gillman   MELROSE   Frederick C. Maker

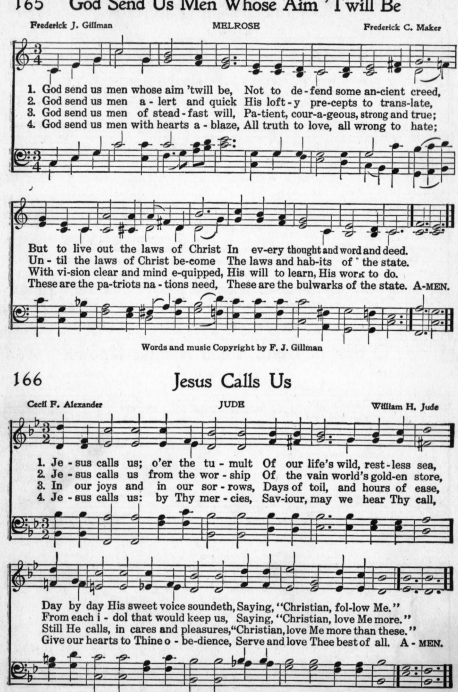

1. God send us men whose aim 'twill be, Not to de-fend some an-cient creed,
2. God send us men a-lert and quick His loft-y pre-cepts to trans-late,
3. God send us men of stead-fast will, Pa-tient, cour-a-geous, strong and true;
4. God send us men with hearts a-blaze, All truth to love, all wrong to hate;

But to live out the laws of Christ In ev-ery thought and word and deed.
Un-til the laws of Christ be-come The laws and hab-its of the state.
With vi-sion clear and mind e-quipped, His will to learn, His work to do.
These are the pa-triots na-tions need, These are the bulwarks of the state. A-MEN.

Words and music Copyright by F. J. Gillman

166 Jesus Calls Us

Cecil F. Alexander   JUDE   William H. Jude

1. Je-sus calls us; o'er the tu-mult Of our life's wild, rest-less sea,
2. Je-sus calls us from the wor-ship Of the vain world's gold-en store,
3. In our joys and in our sor-rows, Days of toil, and hours of ease,
4. Je-sus calls us: by Thy mer-cies, Sav-iour, may we hear Thy call,

Day by day His sweet voice soundeth, Saying, "Christian, fol-low Me."
From each i-dol that would keep us, Saying, "Christian, love Me more."
Still He calls, in cares and pleasures, "Christian, love Me more than these."
Give our hearts to Thine o-be-dience, Serve and love Thee best of all. A-MEN.

The Fathers Built This City

William G. Tarrant   ALFORD   John B. Dykes

1. The fa - thers built this cit - y How man - y years a - go!
2. Yet still the cit - y stand - eth, A hive of toil - ing men,
3. Let all the peo - ple praise Thee, Give all Thy sav - ing health,
4. A com - mon - weal of broth - ers, U - nit - ed, great and small,

And bus - y in its bus - y streets, They hur - ried to and fro;
And moth - er's love makes hap - py home For chil - dren now as then;
Or vain the la - borer's strong right arm And vain the mer - chant's wealth.
Up - on our ban - ner bla - zoned be The char - ter, "Each for all."

The chil - dren played a - round them And sang the songs of yore,
O God of a - ges, help us Such cit - i - zens to be
Send forth Thy light to ban - ish The shad - ows and the shame,
Nor let us cease from bat - tle, Nor wea - ry sheathe the sword,

Till one by one, they fell a - sleep, To work and play no more.
That children's chil - dren here may sing The songs of lib - er - ty.
Till all the civ - ic vir - tues shine A - round our cit - y's name.
Un - til this cit - y is be - come The cit - y of the Lord. A-MEN.

168 Once to Every Man and Nation

TON-Y-BOTEL

James Russell Lowell

Welsh Hymn Melody

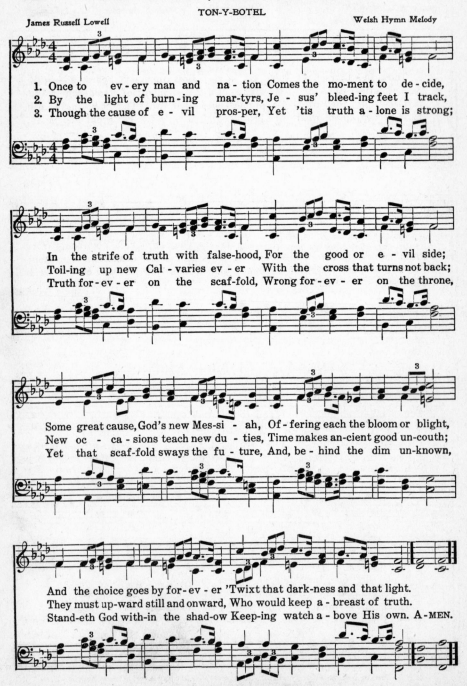

1. Once to ev-ery man and na-tion Comes the mo-ment to de-cide,
2. By the light of burn-ing mar-tyrs, Je-sus' bleed-ing feet I track,
3. Though the cause of e-vil pros-per, Yet 'tis truth a-lone is strong;

In the strife of truth with false-hood, For the good or e-vil side;
Toil-ing up new Cal-varies ev-er With the cross that turns not back;
Truth for-ev-er on the scaf-fold, Wrong for-ev-er on the throne,

Some great cause, God's new Mes-si-ah, Of-fering each the bloom or blight,
New oc-ca-sions teach new du-ties, Time makes an-cient good un-couth;
Yet that scaf-fold sways the fu-ture, And, be-hind the dim un-known,

And the choice goes by for-ev-er 'Twixt that dark-ness and that light.
They must up-ward still and onward, Who would keep a-breast of truth.
Stand-eth God with-in the shad-ow Keep-ing watch a-bove His own. A-MEN.

Where Cross the Crowded Ways of Life 169

Frank Mason North   GERMANY   William Gardiner's "Sacred Melodies"

In moderate time

1. Where cross the crowded ways of life, Where sound the cries of race and clan,
2. In haunts of wretch-ed-ness and need, On shadowed thresholds dark with fears,
3. From ten-der child-hood's helplessness, From woman's grief, man's burdened toil,
4. The cup of wa-ter given for Thee Still holds the freshness of Thy grace;
5. O Mas-ter, from the moun-tain side, Make haste to heal these hearts of pain;
6. Till sons of men shall learn Thy love, And fol-low where Thy feet have trod;

A - bove the noise of self - ish strife, We hear Thy voice, O Son of Man.
From paths where hide the lures of greed, We catch the vi - sion of Thy tears.
From famished souls, from sorrow's stress, Thy heart has nev-er known re-coil.
Yet long these mul-ti-tudes to see The sweet com-pas-sion of Thy face.
A-mong these rest-less throngs a-bide, O tread the cit - y's streets a-gain,
Till glo-rious from Thy heav'n a-bove Shall come the Cit-y of our God. A-MEN.

Rise Up, O Men of God 170

Rev. William Pierson Merrill   FESTAL SONG   William H. Walter

With spirit

1. Rise up, O men of God! Have done with less - er things; Give
2. Rise up, O men of God! His King - dom tar - ries long; Bring
3. Rise up, O men of God! The Church for you doth wait, Her
4. Lift high the cross of Christ! Tread where His feet have trod; As

heart and soul and mind and strength To serve the King of kings.
in the day of broth - er - hood And end the night of wrong.
strength un - e - qual to her task; Rise up, and make her great!
broth - ers of the Son of Man, Rise up, O men of God! A-MEN.

Used by permission of The Presbyterian Tribune, 70 Fifth Avenue, New York
(formerly The Presbyterian Advance)

171 We Thank Thee, Lord, Thy Paths of Service

Calvin W. Laufer   FIELD   Calvin W. Laufer

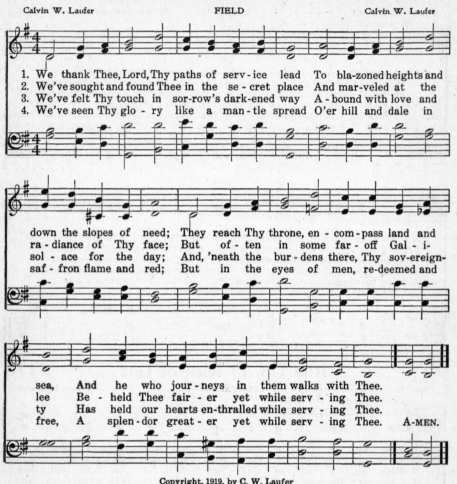

1. We thank Thee, Lord, Thy paths of serv-ice lead To bla-zoned heights and down the slopes of need; They reach Thy throne, en-com-pass land and sea, And he who jour-neys in them walks with Thee.
2. We've sought and found Thee in the se-cret place And mar-veled at the ra-diance of Thy face; But of-ten in some far-off Gal-i-lee Be-held Thee fair-er yet while serv-ing Thee.
3. We've felt Thy touch in sor-row's dark-ened way A-bound with love and sol-ace for the day; And, 'neath the bur-dens there, Thy sov-ereign-ty Has held our hearts en-thralled while serv-ing Thee.
4. We've seen Thy glo-ry like a man-tle spread O'er hill and dale in saf-fron flame and red; But in the eyes of men, re-deemed and free, A splen-dor great-er yet while serv-ing Thee. A-MEN.

Copyright, 1919, by C. W. Laufer

172 O Master, Let Me Walk with Thee

Washington Gladden   MARYTON   H. Percy Smith

1. O Mas-ter, let me walk with Thee In low-ly paths of serv-ice free;
2. Help me the slow of heart to move By some clear, win-ning word of love;
3. Teach me Thy patience! still with Thee In clos-er, dear-er com-pa-ny,
4. In hope that sends a shin-ing ray Far down the fu-ture's broadening way,

O Master, Let Me Walk with Thee

Tell me Thy se-cret; help me bear The strain of toil, the fret of care.
Teach me the way-ward feet to stay, And guide them in the homeward way.
In work that keeps faith sweet and strong, In trust that tri-umphs o - ver wrong;
In peace that on - ly Thou canst give, With Thee, O Mas-ter, let me live. A-MEN.

Light of the World

173

John S. B. Monsell

LIGHT OF THE WORLD

Anon.

1. Light of the world, we hail Thee, Flush-ing the east - ern skies;
2. Light of the world, Thy beau - ty Steals in - to ev - ery heart,
3. Light of the world, il - lu - mine This dark-ened earth of Thine,

Nev - er shall dark-ness veil Thee A - gain from hu - man eyes;
And glo - ri - fies with du - ty Life's poor-est, hum-blest part;
Till ev - ery-thing that's hu - man Be filled with what's di - vine;

Too long, a - las, with-hold - en, Now spread from shore to shore;
Thou rob - est in Thy splen - dor The sim - ple ways of men,
Till ev - ery tongue and na - tion, From sin's do - min - ion free,

Thy light, so glad and gold - en, Shall set on earth no more.
And help-est them to ren - der Light back to Thee a - gain.
Rise in the new cre - a - tion Which springs from love and Thee. A - MEN.

174   # Forward through the Ages

Frederick L. Hosmer   ONWARD   J. W. Barrington

1. Forward through the a-ges In un-bro-ken line, Move the faithful spir-its
2. Wid-er grows the kingdom, Reign of love and light; For it we must la - bor
3. Not a - lone we con-quer, Not a - lone we fall; In each loss or tri-umph

At the call di - vine; Gifts in differing measures, Hearts of one ac-cord,
Till our faith is sight; Prophets have proclaimed it, Martyrs tes - ti - fied,
Lose or tri-umph all. Bound by God's fair pur-pose In one liv - ing whole,

REFRAIN

Man - i - fold the serv-ice, One the sure re - ward.
Po - ets sung its glo - ry, He-roes for it died.   Forward through the a - ges
Move we on to-geth - er To the shin-ing goal.

In un-bro-ken line, Move the faith-ful spir-its At the call di - vine. A-MEN.

From the *Hymn and Tune Book*, Copyright, The Beacon Press, Inc. Used with permission

We've a Story to Tell to the Nations 175

Colin Sterne

Adapted from H. Ernest Nichol

1. We've a sto - ry to tell to the na - tions That shall
2. We've a song to be sung to the na - tions That shall
3. We've a mes - sage to give to the na - tions Who the
4. We've a Sav - iour to show to the na - tions That the

turn their hearts to the right, A sto - ry of truth and mer - cy,
lift their hearts to the Lord, A song that shall con - quer e - vil
Lord who reign-eth a - bove Hath sent us His Son to save us,
path of sor - row hath trod, That all of the world's great peo - ples

A sto - ry of peace and light, A sto - ry of peace and light.
And shat - ter the spear and sword, And shat - ter the spear and sword.
And show us that God is love, And show us that God is love.
Might come to the truth of God, Might come to the truth of God.

CHORUS

For the dark-ness shall turn to dawn - ing, And the dawn-ing to noon-day bright,

And Christ's great king-dom shall come to earth, The king-dom of love and light.

176 When Wilt Thou Save the People

Ebenezer Elliott   COMMONWEALTH   Josiah Booth

1. When wilt Thou save the peo - ple? O God of mer - cy, when?
2. Shall crime bring crime for - ev - er, Strength aid - ing still the strong?
3. When wilt Thou save the peo - ple? O God of mer - cy, when?

Not kings and lords, but na - tions, Not thrones and crowns, but men!
Is it Thy will, O Fa - ther, That man shall toil for wrong?
The peo - ple, Lord, the peo - ple, Not thrones and crowns, but men!

Flowers of Thy heart, O God, are they; Let them not pass, like weeds, a - way,
"No," say Thy mountains; "No," Thy skies; Man's cloud-ed sun shall bright-ly rise,
God save the peo - ple; Thine they are, Thy chil - dren, as Thine an - gels fair:

Their her - it - age a sun - less day: God save the peo - ple!
And songs as - cend, in - stead of sighs: God save the peo - ple!
From vice, op - pres-sion and de - spair, God save the peo - ple! A-MEN.

O Zion, Haste

Mary A. Thomson   TIDINGS   James Walch

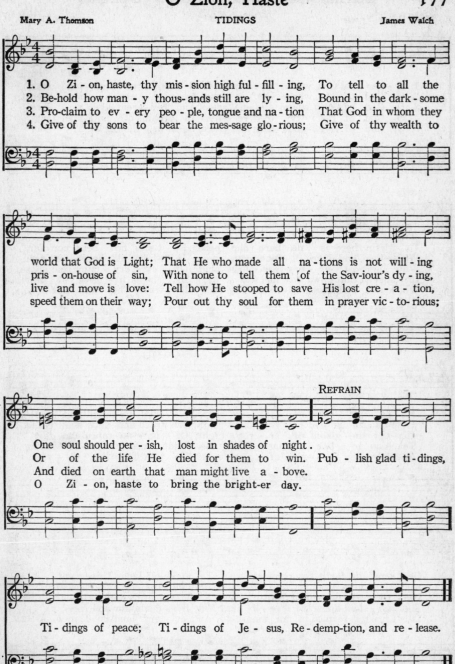

1. O Zi - on, haste, thy mis - sion high ful - fill - ing, To tell to all the
2. Be-hold how man - y thous-ands still are ly - ing, Bound in the dark-some
3. Pro-claim to ev - ery peo - ple, tongue and na - tion That God in whom they
4. Give of thy sons to bear the mes-sage glo-rious; Give of thy wealth to

world that God is Light; That He who made all na - tions is not will - ing
pris - on-house of sin, With none to tell them of the Sav-iour's dy - ing,
live and move is love: Tell how He stooped to save His lost cre - a - tion,
speed them on their way; Pour out thy soul for them in prayer vic - to- rious;

REFRAIN

One soul should per - ish, lost in shades of night.
Or of the life He died for them to win. Pub - lish glad ti - dings,
And died on earth that man might live a - bove.
O Zi - on, haste to bring the bright-er day.

Ti - dings of peace; Ti - dings of Je - sus, Re - demp-tion, and re - lease.

178 Eternal God, Whose Power Upholds

Henry Hallam Tweedy   SARAH   Rhys Thomas

1. E - ter - nal God, whose power up-holds Both flower and flam - ing star,
2. O God of love, whose Spir - it wakes In ev - ery hu - man breast,
3. O God of truth, whom sci - ence seeks And rev - erent souls a - dore,
4. O God of beau - ty, oft re-vealed In dreams of hu - man art,
5. O God of right - eous - ness and grace, Seen in the Christ, Thy Son,

To whom there is no here nor there, No time, no near nor far,
Whom love, and love a - lone can know, In whom all hearts find rest,
Who light-est ev - ery ear - nest mind Of ev - ery clime and shore,
In speech that flows to mel - o - dy, In ho - li - ness of heart,
Whose life and death re - veal Thy face, By whom Thy will was done,

No al - ien race, no for - eign shore, No child un-sought, un - known,
Help us to spread Thy gra - cious reign Till greed and hate shall cease,
Dis - pel the gloom of er - ror's night, Of ig - no - rance and fear,
Teach us to ban all ug - li - ness That blinds our eyes to Thee,
In - spire Thy her - alds of good news To live Thy life di - vine,

Oh, send us forth, Thy prophets true, To make all lands Thine own!
And kind - ness dwell in hu-man hearts, And all the earth find peace!
Un - til true wis - dom from a - bove Shall make life's pathway clear!
Till all shall know the love - li - ness Of lives made fair and free.
Till Christ is formed in all man-kind And ev - ery land is Thine! A-MEN.

At Length There Dawns the Glorious Day 179

Ozora S. Davis   ALL SAINTS NEW   Henry S. Cutler

1. At length there dawns the glo-rious day By proph-ets long fore-told,
2. For what are sun-dering strains of blood, Or an-cient caste and creed?
3. One com-mon faith u-nites us all, We seek one com-mon goal;

At length the cho-rus clear-er grows That shep-herds heard of old.
One claim u-nites all men in God To serve each hu-man need.
One ten-der com-fort broods up-on The strug-gling hu-man soul.

The day of dawn-ing broth-er-hood Breaks on our ea-ger eyes,
Then here to-geth-er, broth-er-men, We pledge the Lord a-new
To this clear call of broth-er-hood Our hearts re-spon-sive ring;

And hu-man ha-treds flee be-fore The ra-diant east-ern skies.
Our loy-al love, our stal-wart faith, Our serv-ice strong and true.
We join the glo-rious new cru-sade Of our great Lord and King. A-MEN.

180 God of the Nations, Near and Far

John Haynes Holmes   SAWLEY   James Walch

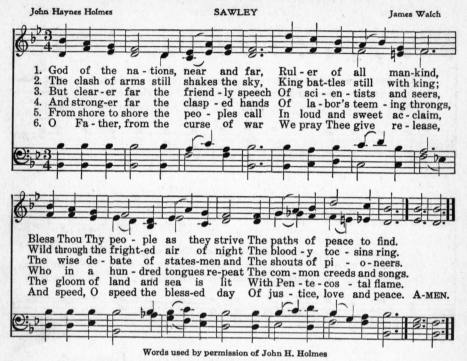

1. God of the na - tions, near and far, Rul - er of all man-kind,
2. The clash of arms still shakes the sky, King bat-tles still with king;
3. But clear - er far the friend - ly speech Of sci - en - tists and seers,
4. And strong-er far the clasp - ed hands Of la - bor's teem - ing throngs,
5. From shore to shore the peo - ples call In loud and sweet ac - claim,
6. O Fa - ther, from the curse of war We pray Thee give re - lease,

Bless Thou Thy peo - ple as they strive The paths of peace to find.
Wild through the fright-ed air of night The blood - y toc - sins ring.
The wise de - bate of states-men and The shouts of pi - o - neers.
Who in a hun - dred tongues re-peat The com - mon creeds and songs.
The gloom of land and sea is lit With Pen - te - cos - tal flame.
And speed, O speed the bless-ed day Of jus - tice, love and peace. A-MEN.

Words used by permission of John H. Holmes

181 In Christ There Is No East or West

John Oxenham   Alexander R. Reinagle

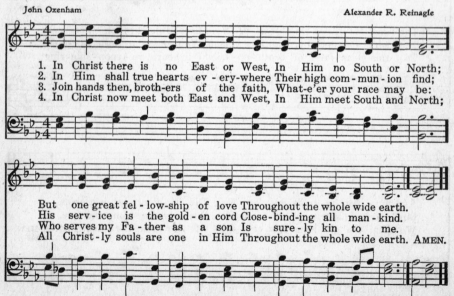

1. In Christ there is no East or West, In Him no South or North;
2. In Him shall true hearts ev - ery-where Their high com - mun - ion find;
3. Join hands then, broth-ers of the faith, What-e'er your race may be:
4. In Christ now meet both East and West, In Him meet South and North;

But one great fel - low-ship of love Throughout the whole wide earth.
His serv - ice is the gold - en cord Close-bind-ing all man - kind.
Who serves my Fa - ther as a son Is sure - ly kin to me.
All Christ - ly souls are one in Him Throughout the whole wide earth. AMEN.

Jesus Shall Reign

182

From Psalm 72
Isaac Watts

DUKE STREET

John Hatton

1. Je - sus shall reign where'er the sun Does his suc-ces-sive jour-neys run;
2. To Him shall end-less prayer be made, And prais-es throng to crown His head;
3. Peo-ple and realms of ev - er - y tongue Dwell on His love with sweet-est song,
4. Blessings a-bound wher-e'er He reigns; The prisoner leaps to lose his chains,
5. Let ev - er - y crea - ture rise and bring Pe - cul - iar hon - ors to our King,

His Kingdom stretch from shore to shore, Till moons shall wax and wane no more.
His Name, like sweet perfume, shall rise With every morn-ing sac - ri - fice.
And in-fant voic-es shall pro-claim Their early bless-ings on His Name.
The wea - ry find e - ter - nal rest, And all the sons of want are blest.
An - gels de-scend with songs a - gain, And earth repeat the loud A - men! A-MEN.

Fling Out the Banner! Let It Float

183

George W. Doane

WALTHAM (Doane)

John B. Calkin

1. Fling out the ban - ner! let it float Sky-ward and sea-ward, high and wide;
2. Fling out the ban - ner! dis-tant lands Shall see from far the glo-rious sight,
3. Fling out the ban - ner! sin-sick souls That sink and per - ish in the strife,
4. Fling out the ban - ner! let it float Sky-ward and sea-ward, high and wide;
5. Fling out the ban - ner! wide and high, Sea-ward and sky-ward, let it shine:

The sun that lights its shin-ing folds, The cross on which the Saviour died.
And na-tions, crowding to be born, Bap-tize their spir-its in its light.
Shall touch in faith its ra-diant hem, And spring im-mor-tal in - to life.
Our glo - ry, on - ly in the cross; Our on - ly hope, the Cru - ci - fied.
Nor skill, nor might, nor mer-it ours; We con-quer on - ly in that sign. A-MEN.

184 Go, Labor on: Spend, and Be Spent

Horatius Bonar

MISSIONARY CHANT

Heinrich Christopher Zeuner

1. Go, la-bor on: spend, and be spent, Thy joy to do the Fa-ther's will:
2. Go, la-bor on: 'tis not for nought; Thy earth-ly loss is heaven-ly gain:
3. Go, la-bor on while it is day: The world's dark night is hastening on;
4. Toil on, faint not, keep watch and pray, Be wise the err-ing soul to win;

It is the way the Mas-ter went; Should not the servant tread it still?
Men heed thee, love thee, praise thee not; The Mas-ter praises: what are men?
Speed, speed thy work, cast sloth away; It is not thus that souls are won.
Go forth in-to the world's highway, Com-pel the wanderer to come in. A-MEN.

185 O God of Love, O King of Peace

Henry W. Baker

HESPERUS

Henry W. Baker

1. O God of love, O King of peace, Make wars throughout the world to cease;
2. Re-mem-ber, Lord, Thy works of old, The won-ders that our fa-thers told;
3. Whom shall we trust but Thee, O Lord? Where rest but on Thy faith-ful word?
4. Where saints and angels dwell a-bove, All hearts are knit in ho-ly love;

The wrath of sin-ful man re-strain, Give peace, O God, give peace a-gain!
Re-mem-ber not our sin's dark stain, Give peace, O God, give peace a-gain!
None ev-er called on Thee in vain, Give peace, O God, give peace a-gain!
O bind us in that heavenly chain; Give peace, O God, give peace a-gain! A-MEN.

O Beautiful for Spacious Skies

Katharine Lee Bates   MATERNA   Samuel A. Ward

1. O beau - ti - ful for spa - cious skies, For am - ber waves of grain,
2. O beau - ti - ful for pil - grim feet, Whose stern, im - pas-sioned stress
3. O beau - ti - ful for he - roes proved In lib - er - at - ing strife,
4. O beau - ti - ful for pa - triot dream That sees be - yond the years

For pur - ple moun - tain maj - es - ties A - bove the fruit - ed plain!
A thor-ough - fare for free - dom beat A - cross the wil - der - ness!
Who more than self their coun - try loved, And mer - cy more than life!
Thine al - a - bas - ter cit - ies gleam, Un - dimmed by hu - man tears!

A - mer - i - ca! A - mer - i - ca! God shed His grace on thee,
A - mer - i - ca! A - mer - i - ca! God mend thine ev - ery flaw,
A - mer - i - ca! A - mer - i - ca! May God thy gold re - fine
A - mer - i - ca! A - mer - i - ca! God shed His grace on thee,

And crown thy good with broth - er - hood From sea to shin - ing sea!
Con - firm thy soul in self - con-trol, Thy lib - er - ty in law!
Till all suc - cess be no - ble-ness And ev - ery gain di - vine!
And crown thy good with broth - er - hood From sea to shin - ing sea! A-MEN.

187 God of Our Fathers, Whose Almighty Hand

NATIONAL HYMN

Daniel C. Roberts

George W. Warren

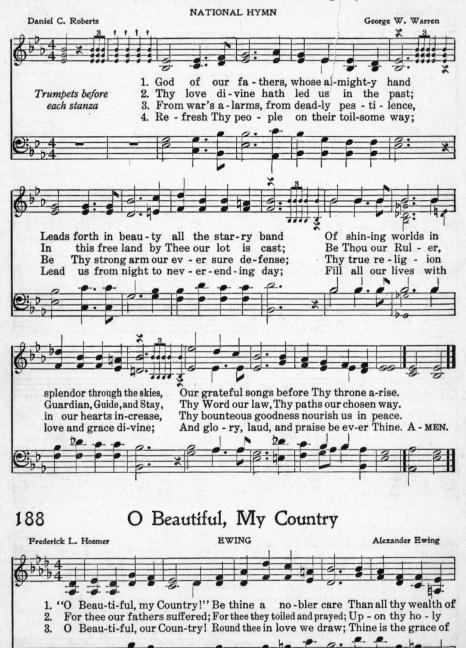

Trumpets before
each stanza

1. God of our fa - thers, whose al-might-y hand
2. Thy love di - vine hath led us in the past;
3. From war's a - larms, from dead-ly pes - ti - lence,
4. Re - fresh Thy peo - ple on their toil-some way;

Leads forth in beau - ty all the star-ry band   Of shin-ing worlds in
In   this free land by Thee our lot is cast;   Be Thou our Rul - er,
Be   Thy strong arm our ev - er sure de-fense;   Thy true re - lig - ion
Lead   us from night to nev - er-end-ing day;   Fill all our lives with

splendor through the skies,   Our grateful songs before Thy throne a-rise.
Guardian, Guide, and Stay,   Thy Word our law, Thy paths our chosen way.
in our hearts in-crease,   Thy bounteous goodness nourish us in peace.
love and grace di-vine;   And glo - ry, laud, and praise be ev-er Thine. A - MEN.

188   O Beautiful, My Country

Frederick L. Hosmer

EWING

Alexander Ewing

1. "O Beau-ti-ful, my Country!" Be thine a   no-bler care Than all thy wealth of
2. For thee our fathers suffered; For thee they toiled and prayed; Up - on thy ho - ly
3. O Beau-ti-ful, our Coun-try! Round thee in love we draw; Thine is the grace of

O Beautiful, My Country

commerce, Thy harvests wav-ing fair: Be it thy pride to lift up The man-hood
al - tar Their willing lives they laid. Thou hast no common birthright, Grand memories
free-dom, The maj-es-ty of law. Be righteousness thy scep-tre, Jus-tice thy

of the poor; Be thou to the op-press-ed Fair Freedom's o-pen door.
on thee shine; The blood of pil-grim na-tions Commingled flows in thine.
di - a - dem; And on thy shin-ing forehead Be peace the crowning gem! A-MEN.

My Country, 'Tis of Thee   189

Samuel F. Smith   AMERICA   Henry Carey

1. My coun-try, 'tis of thee, Sweet land of lib - er - ty, Of thee I sing: Land where my
2. My na - tive coun-try, thee, Land of the no - ble, free, Thy name I love: I love thy
3. Let mu - sic swell the breeze, And ring from all the trees Sweet freedom's song: Let mor-tal
4. Our fa-thers' God, to Thee, Au - thor of lib - er - ty, To Thee we sing: Long may our

fa - thers died, Land of the pilgrim's pride, From ev-ery mountain side Let free-dom ring!
rocks and rills, Thy woods and templed hills; My heart with rapture thrills, Like that a-bove.
tongues awake; Let all that breathe partake; Let rocks their silence break, The sound prolong.
land be bright With freedom's ho-ly light; Protect us by Thy might, Great God, our King! A- MEN.

190 God Save America

William G. Ballantine · RUSSIAN HYMN · Alexis T. Lwoff

1. God save A - mer - i - ca! New world of glo - ry,
2. God save A - mer - i - ca! Here may all rac - es
3. God save A - mer - i - ca! Broth - er - hood ban - ish
4. God save A - mer - i - ca! Bear - ing the ol - ive,
5. God save A - mer - i - ca! 'Mid all her splen - dors,

New - born to free - dom and knowl - edge and power,
Min - gle to - geth - er as chil - dren of God;
Wail of the work - er and curse of the crushed;
Hers be the bless - ing the peace - mak - ers prove,
Save her from pride and from lux - u - ry;

Lift - ing the towers of her light - ning - lit cit - ies
Found - ing an em - pire on broth - er - ly kind - ness,
Joy break in songs from her ju - bi - lant mil - lions,
Call - ing the na - tions to glad fed - er - a - tion,
Throne in her heart the un - seen and e - ter - nal;

Where the flood - tides of hu - man - i - ty roar.
E - qual in lib - er - ty, made of one blood.
Hail - ing the day when all dis - cords are hushed.
Lead - ing the world in the tri - umph of love.
Right be her might and the truth make her free. A - MEN.

Used by permission of William G. Ballantine

All Beautiful the March of Days

SHACKELFORD

Frances W. Wile

Frederick H. Cheeswright

1. All beau-ti-ful the march of days, As sea-sons come and go;
2. O'er white ex-pans-es spar-kling pure The ra-diant morns un-fold;
3. O Thou from whose un-fath-omed law The year in beau-ty flows,

The hand that shaped the rose hath wrought The crys-tal of the snow;
The sol-emn splen-dors of the night Burn bright-er through the cold;
Thy-self the vi-sion pass-ing by In crys-tal and in rose,

Hath sent the hoar-y frost of heaven, The flow-ing wa-ter sealed,
Life mounts in ev-'ry throb-bing vein, Love deep-ens round the hearth,
Day un-to day doth ut-ter speech, And night to night pro-claim,

And laid a si-lent love-li-ness On hill and wood and field.
And clear-er sounds the an-gel-hymn, "Good-will to men on earth."
In ev-er-chang-ing words of light, The won-der of Thy name. A-MEN.

192 The Summer Days Are Come Again

FOREST GREEN

Samuel Longfellow

English traditional melody

1. The sum-mer days are come a-gain; Once more the glad earth yields
2. The sum-mer days are come a-gain; The birds are on the wing;

Her gold-en wealth of ripen-ing grain, And glow of clo-ver fields,
God's prais-es, in their lov-ing strain, Un-con-scious-ly they sing:

And deep-ening shade of sum-mer woods, And glow of sum-mer air,
We know who giv-eth all the good That doth our cup o'er-brim,

And wind-ing thoughts, and hap-py moods Of love and joy and prayer.
For sum-mer joy in field and wood We lift our song to Him. A-MEN.

Tune from *The English Hymnal.* Used by permission of the Oxford University Press

O Blessed Day of Motherhood! 193

Ernest F. McGregor MATER Arthur Depew

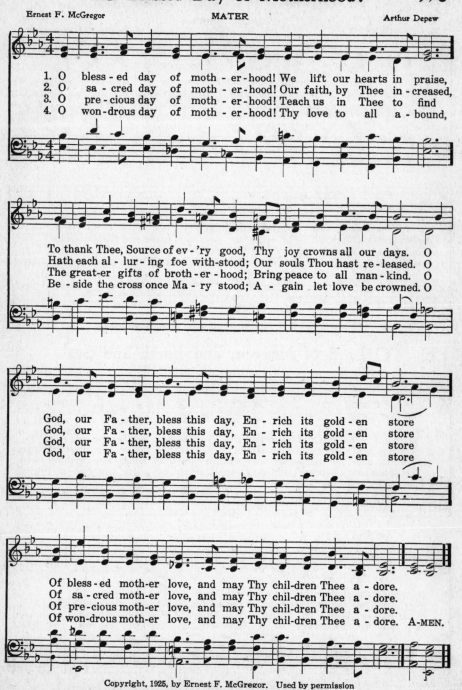

1. O bless-ed day of moth-er-hood! We lift our hearts in praise,
2. O sa-cred day of moth-er-hood! Our faith, by Thee in-creased,
3. O pre-cious day of moth-er-hood! Teach us in Thee to find
4. O won-drous day of moth-er-hood! Thy love to all a-bound,

To thank Thee, Source of ev-'ry good, Thy joy crowns all our days. O
Hath each al-lur-ing foe with-stood; Our souls Thou hast re-leased. O
The great-er gifts of broth-er-hood; Bring peace to all man-kind. O
Be-side the cross once Ma-ry stood; A-gain let love be crowned. O

God, our Fa-ther, bless this day, En-rich its gold-en store
God, our Fa-ther, bless this day, En-rich its gold-en store
God, our Fa-ther, bless this day, En-rich its gold-en store
God, our Fa-ther, bless this day, En-rich its gold-en store

Of bless-ed moth-er love, and may Thy chil-dren Thee a-dore.
Of sa-cred moth-er love, and may Thy chil-dren Thee a-dore.
Of pre-cious moth-er love, and may Thy chil-dren Thee a-dore.
Of won-drous moth-er love, and may Thy chil-dren Thee a-dore. A-MEN.

194   O Father, Thou Who Givest All

John Hayes Holmes   BELOIT   Carl G. Reissiger

1. O Fa - ther, Thou who giv - est all The boun-ty of Thy per - fect love, We
2. We thank Thee for the grace of home, For mother's love and fa - ther's care; For
3. For eyes to see and ears to hear, For hands to serve and arms to lift, For
4. For faith to con-quer doubt and fear, For love to an - swer ev - ery call, For

thank Thee that up - on us fall Such ten - der bless-ings from a - bove.
friends and teach-ers, all who come Our joys and hopes and fears to share;
shoul - ders broad and strong to bear, For feet to run on er-rands swift.
strength to do, and will to dare, We thank Thee, O Thou Lord of all. A-MEN.

Words Copyright by John Haynes Holmes. Used by permission

195   O Lord of Heaven, and Earth and Sea

Christopher Wordsworth   ALMSGIVING   John B. Dykes

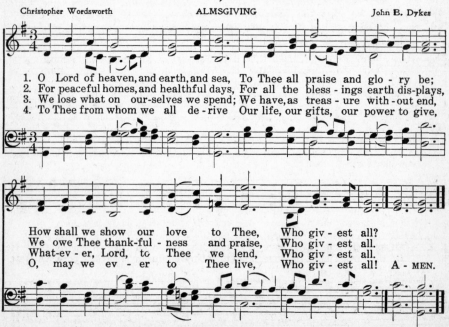

1. O Lord of heaven, and earth, and sea, To Thee all praise and glo - ry be;
2. For peaceful homes, and healthful days, For all the bless - ings earth dis-plays,
3. We lose what on our-selves we spend; We have, as treas - ure with - out end,
4. To Thee from whom we all de - rive Our life, our gifts, our power to give,

How shall we show our love to Thee, Who giv - est all?
We owe Thee thank-ful - ness and praise, Who giv - est all.
What-ev - er, Lord, to Thee we lend, Who giv - est all.
O, may we ev - er to Thee live, Who giv - est all! A - MEN.

We Plow the Fields, and Scatter

Matthias Claudius
Tr. by Jane M. Campbell

DRESDEN

Johann A. P. Schultz

1. We plow the fields, and scat-ter The good seed on the land, But it is
2. He on-ly is the Mak-er Of all things near and far, He paints the
3. We thank Thee, then, O Fa-ther, For all things bright and good, The seed-time

fed and wa-tered By God's al-might-y hand; He sends the snow in
way-side flow-er, He lights the eve-ning star; The winds and waves o-
and the har-vest, Our life, our health, our food; Ac-cept the gifts we

win-ter, The warmth to swell the grain, The breez-es and the sun-shine, And
bey Him, By Him the birds are fed; Much more to us, His chil-dren, He
of-fer, For all Thy love im-parts, And what Thou most de-sir-est, Our

REFRAIN

soft re-fresh-ing rain.
gives our dai-ly bread. All good gifts a-round us Are sent from heaven a-
hum-ble, thank-ful hearts.

bove; Then thank the Lord, O thank the Lord For all...... His love. A-MEN.

197 Come, Ye Thankful People

Henry Alford · ST. GEORGE'S, WINDSOR · George J. Elvey

1. Come, ye thank-ful peo-ple, come, Raise the song of har-vest-home:
2. All the world is God's own field, Fruit un-to His praise to yield;
3. For the Lord our God shall come, And shall take His har-vest home;
4. E-ven so, Lord, quick-ly come To Thy fi-nal har-vest-home;

All is safe-ly gath-ered in, Ere the win-ter storms be-gin;
Wheat and tares to-geth-er sown, Un-to joy or sor-row grown;
From His field shall in that day All of-fens-es purge a-way;
Gath-er Thou Thy peo-ple in, Free from sor-row, free from sin;

God, our Ma-ker, doth pro-vide For our wants to be sup-plied:
First the blade, and then the ear, Then the full corn shall ap-pear:
Give His an-gels charge at last In the fire the tares to cast;
There, for-ev-er pu-ri-fied, In Thy pres-ence to a-bide:

Come to God's own tem-ple, come, Raise the song of har-vest-home.
Lord of har-vest, grant that we Whole-some grain and pure may be.
But the fruit-ful ears to store In His gar-ner ev-er-more.
Come, with all Thine an-gels, come, Raise the glo-rious har-vest-home.

A-MEN.

Now Thank We All Our God

Martin Rinkart
Tr. by Catherine Winkworth

NUN DANKET

Johann Cruger

1. Now thank we all our God With heart and hands and voic - es,
2. O may this boun-teous God Through all our life be near us,
3. All praise and thanks to God The Fa - ther now be giv - en,

Who won-drous things hath done, In whom His world re - joic - es;
With ev - er joy - ful hearts And bless - ed peace to cheer us;
The Son and Him who reigns With them in high - est heav - en,

Who from our moth - ers' arms Hath blessed us on our way
And keep us in His grace, And guide us when per - plexed,
The one e - ter - nal God, Whom earth and heaven a - dore,

With count-less gifts of love, And still is ours to - day.
And free us from all ills In this world and the next.
For thus it was, is now, And shall be ev - er - more. A - MEN.

199 Steal Away

STEAL AWAY

Negro Melody

CHORUS

Steal a-way, steal a-way, Steal a-way to Je-sus. Steal a-way, steal away home,

SOLO

I ain't got long to stay here.
1. My Lord calls me, He calls me by the
2. Green trees are bend-ing, Poor sin-ner stands a-
3. My Lord calls me, He calls me by the

CHORUS

thun-der; The trumpet sounds with-in-a my soul! I ain't got long to stay here.
trembling; The trumpet sounds with-in-a my soul! I ain't got long to stay here.
lightning; The trumpet sounds with-in-a my soul! I ain't got long to stay here.

200 We Are Climbing Jacob's Ladder

Negro Spiritual

1. We are climb-ing Ja-cob's lad-der, lad-der, We are climb-ing Ja-cob's lad-der,
2. Ev-ery round goes high-er, high-er, high-er, Ev-ery round goes high-er, high-er,
3. Climbing up from earth to heav-en, heaven, Climbing up from earth to heav-en,

lad-der, We are climb-ing Ja-cob's lad-der, Sol-diers of the cross.
high-er, We are climb-ing Ja-cob's lad-der, Sol-diers of the cross.
heaven, We are climb-ing Ja-cob's lad-der, Sol-diers of the cross.

Lord, I Want to Be a Christian

Negro Spiritual

SOLO / CHORUS / REFRAIN

1. Lord, I want to be a Chris-tian In my heart, in my
2. Lord, I want to be more lov-ing In my heart, in my
3. Lord, I want to be more ho-ly In my heart, in my
4. I don't want to be like Ju-das In my heart, in my
5. Lord, I want to be like Je-sus In my heart, in my

heart, Lord, I want to be a Chris-tian In my heart.
heart, Lord, I want to be more lov-ing In my heart.
heart, Lord, I want to be more ho-ly In my heart.
heart, I don't want to be like Ju-das In my heart.
heart, Lord, I want to be like Je-sus In my heart.

In my heart,.............. In my heart,..............
In my heart, In my heart,

Lord, I want to be a Chris-tian In my heart.
Lord, I want to be more lov-ing In my heart.
Lord, I want to be more ho-ly In my heart.
I don't want to be like Ju-das In my heart.
Lord, I want to be like Je-sus In my heart.

202 Praise God, from Whom All Blessings Flow

Thomas Ken OLD HUNDREDTH Louis Bourgeois, Genevan Psalter

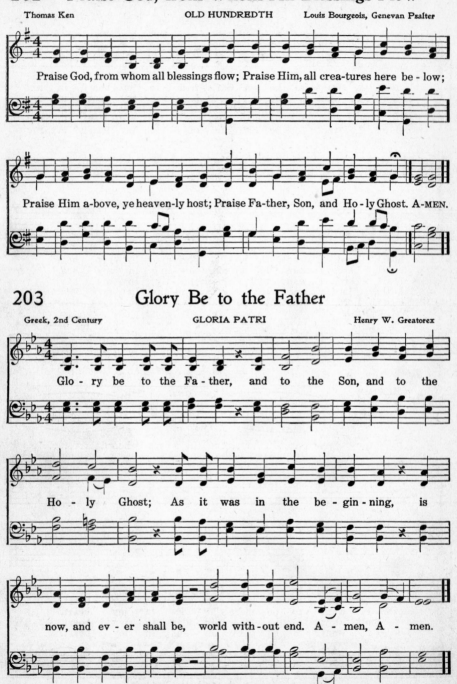

Praise God, from whom all blessings flow; Praise Him, all crea-tures here be - low;

Praise Him a-bove, ye heaven-ly host; Praise Fa-ther, Son, and Ho - ly Ghost. A-MEN.

203 Glory Be to the Father

Greek, 2nd Century GLORIA PATRI Henry W. Greatorex

Glo - ry be to the Fa - ther, and to the Son, and to the

Ho - ly Ghost; As it was in the be - gin - ning, is

now, and ev - er shall be, world with - out end. A - men, A - men.

The Lord Is In His Holy Temple 204

QUAM DILECTA

George F. Root

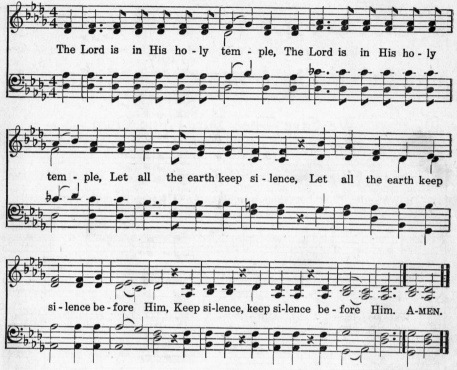

The Lord is in His ho-ly tem-ple, The Lord is in His ho-ly tem-ple, Let all the earth keep si-lence, Let all the earth keep si-lence be-fore Him, Keep si-lence, keep si-lence be-fore Him. A-MEN.

Hear Our Prayer, O Lord 205

George Whelpton

Hear our prayer, O Lord, Hear our prayer, O Lord, In-cline Thine ear to us, And grant us Thy peace. A-MEN.

Copyright by George Whelpton. Used by permission

206 Holy, Holy, Holy

SANCTUS

From "The Holy City"
Alfred R. Gaul

Ho-ly, ho - ly, ho-ly, Lord of hosts: Holy, ho - ly, ho-ly is the Lord of hosts. A-MEN.

207 We Give Thee But Thine Own

SCHUMANN

William Walsham How

Mason and Webb's
"Cantica Laudis," Boston

1. We give Thee but Thine own, What-e'er the gift may be: All
2. May we Thy boun - ties thus As stew-ards true re - ceive, And

that we have is Thine a - lone, A trust, O Lord, from Thee.
glad - ly, as Thou bless-est us, To Thee our first-fruits give. A-MEN.

208 All Things Come of Thee, O Lord

Offertory Sentence

Arr. from Beethoven

All things *come* of Thee, O Lord; and of Thine *own* have we giv-en Thee. A-MEN.

209 DRESDEN AMEN

pp cres.

A-men, A - men.

210 THREEFOLD AMEN

A - men, A - men, A - - men.

Worship

WHAT IS WORSHIP?

The story is told of a man who was entirely self-centered. He lived enclosed in mirrors; everywhere he looked he saw himself. Then appreciation, admiration, adoration, and reverence entered into this man's life and grew until the mirrors became windows through which he looked out and beyond to something other and greater than himself.

A person is close to worship when beauty overwhelms him; when his ambitions and worries are silenced by wonder; when he follows a great thought back and back or on and on and feels the thrill of discovery; when there is deep joy in mutual love, as between parent and child; when there is a decisive victory for right, a victory greater than the person thought he had the power to attain. But in all of these, if there is no sensing of a conscious relationship to the God who has given men the capacity to be overwhelmed by beauty, silenced by wonder, to thrill with intellectual creativity, to love and to make choices, then worship is near but not achieved. Man worships when he gives himself to something other and greater than himself.

The object of Christian worship is the God of Jesus. To worship means to communicate with Him, to declare and adore His worth (worth-ship) and to discover in close communion and fellowship with Him what His will is for man and for His world. The test of a worship experience comes in answer to the question "To what extent has it brought about a harmony of wills, the submission of our wills to the will of God?" This hymnal is dedicated to the task of helping Christian worshipers to worship worthily.

WHY WORSHIP?

When we ask the question, "Why Worship?" we find a number of answers, not all of equal value, but all significant, for each can be verified through observation and experience. First of all, men worship because of certain impulses or drives within them which have been given to all members of the human family by God: such impulses as fear, awe, wonder, curiosity, the desire to be together, the sense of beauty, and others. Again there are those who worship because it has become habit or custom; some because of the training they have received; and some because of the example of others whom they admire greatly. Unless worship has become something more than custom or conformity, many of this group fail to participate in group worship when the situation, location or type of worship is changed.

Finally, there is that group of worshipers who worship because they have experienced the values of true worship and have been reinforced and strengthened by them. They have definite convictions and beliefs about the kind of God who is the Creator and Sustainer and Redeemer of all life, convictions which make for an inner compulsion to worship. They cannot help but worship—they cannot do otherwise!

WHAT HINDERS REAL WORSHIP?

Even though Christian people set aside a time and place to worship God together there are still many hindrances to their worship. Some of these hindrances are within the persons themselves, others are outside of the persons in either the setting for the worship or the service itself.

Other thoughts crowd in upon an individual, making him self-conscious rather than God-conscious; many people attend services unexpectant of anything happening to them or to other worshipers, as if anyone could possibly meet God in worship and be the same thereafter. Again, there are the people who do not want to be too closely in tune with God and His plan for the human family, because of what it will cost them. Still others who have not been confronted with big enough issues and problems to sense their own insufficiency are hindered by a kind of self-sufficiency and self-reliance. And some persons fail to worship because they lack faith in a real God. All these are hindrances within the person.

There are also many outside distractions that hinder worship. Among these that need to be removed or changed are: mechanical features of a service which distract one's attention; the vocabulary of worship which is unfamiliar or meaningless to the worshiper; certain features of the service which result in a negative reaction; insufficient place given for personal participation and time for private prayer; a leader who conducts but who himself fails to worship through the service.

In addition to the above we must face the tremendous force of ignorance of the meaning of worship. Because of the lack of training in the home and the church, the church school and youth group that uses this hymnal will be confronted with an almost unlimited opportunity and responsibility for leadership in significant growth in the experience of worship.

HOW WORSHIP?

ELEMENTS OF WORSHIP:—Down through the centuries of Christian history men have used many different ways or channels through which to give expression to their worship. Some of the most important of these are:

Architecture and Symbolism:—Someone has called architecture "frozen poetry" and many of our worship settings are frozen-prose with no lift to them whatsoever. It is possible to worship God in a barn, at a manger underneath a haystack or in the catacombs. There is a significant difference, however, between a barren square room with flat windows and a long narrow, high chapel with arched windows reaching upward as a setting in which to worship the God of heaven and earth, week after week. Even in a very plain room it is possible to confront the worshipers not only with blank walls and ideas spoken and sung, but with the rich symbolism of the Church; an altar, a cross and an open Bible. The place where we worship is important, but never all important.

Music:—Music ranks highest in the scale of the arts and has always been a handmaid of religion. Quiet, well chosen music at the opening of the service helps a mixed group of people who have come from many disconcerting experiences to become molded into a worshiping unit. It sets the mood of the hour. During the offertory, undergirding guided meditation, at times as an instrumental response to prayers, and again at the close of the service it is an invaluable expression of worship. The music of many of the hymns in this hymnal as well as other simple arrangements of great religious music may be used. A pipe organ or a piano, with several stringed instruments, has been found to be more helpful for group worship than an orchestra.

Poetry:—This is man's attempt at music in word-symbols, and as his high expression of thought and aspiration it will always find a prominent place in worship. Great worship is always more poetic than prosaic.

Hymns:—Hymns are a combination of music and poetry: great religious ideas empowered through the emotions touched with music. Next to the Bible the hymnal is our most significant and useful medium of worship. Children and youth who learn to know, to use and to love the great hymns of the Church, have a way of expressing their worship of God throughout their lives. Interpreting the experience out of which the text of a hymn or hymn tune came is an important part of its meaningful use in worship. This interpretation may be given in the worship service or at some other time.

Prayers:—Prayer is the very heart of the worship experience. It is conversation with God in which we both speak and listen. Through prayers we express our adoration, confession, thanksgiving, petition and intercession and dedication.

Because it is such a tremendous thing for a leader to lead a group in prayer, not to pray for them, or at them, but to help them express their own deepest desires and needs, all public prayers need to be carefully prepared. There will be free and spontaneous prayers, silent prayers, guided thought prayers, hymn prayers sung quietly, the reverent reading of some of the great classic prayers of the church in all ages, either in unison or by the leader, and litanies in which the worshipers respond with the same phrase. Almost every service will contain an invocation prayer, seeking God's presence and blessing; a prayer before or after the offering; and the benediction prayer.

Scripture and Devotional Literature:—Since the days of the early Christians in the catacombs the reading of the Old and the New Testament Scriptures has had a central part in all group worship. If the Scripture is read by the leader, he may very briefly give the Biblical setting of the passage. At other times the reading is done responsively or antiphonally; and certain of the well-known Psalms and Beatitudes may be read in unison. Intelligent selection is all important. New Testament passages should perhaps be dominant and Old Testament readings should be seen through New Testament eyes. It might be well to keep a record of the passages used week after week in order to avoid repetition. God has spoken through men in every century and continues to do so today. Readings from the great store of religious literature from Augustine to Kagawa's meditations may also find their place in our services of worship.

Art Pictures:—Art, like music, is another handmaid of religion. Today, more than ever before there are valuable resources for worship in great religious pictures, both ancient and modern. Excellent interpretations and meditations for both stereopticon slides and large framed pictures, well-lighted, and placed on an easel before the worshiping group, are available.

Drama:—Drama had its beginning in the Church. It was widely used in the early Christian worship. It became secularized as it left the sanctuary and went into the arenas and forums to take care of the overflow crowds. Today there is a revival of the presentation of religious truth through drama. A growing literature of drama for worship is available for exploration and use in the Church with the most meager resources and equipment. Pageantry is one form of religious drama.

Silence:—"Be still and know that I am God", is an insight greatly needed in Protestant Church worship. Many of our worship services are doing or saying something every minute, with little or no quiet spaces to listen while God speaks. One great body of Christians uses this channel for worship almost exclusively. Short periods of silence can be helpfully used after the call to worship . . . "let all the earth keep silence" . . . ; before a spoken prayer; between the various thoughts in a guided meditation; and after the benediction.

Stories, Talks, Testimonies:—Stories with a religious message, well-chosen for the particular worshiping group; talks based on great religious themes and carefully worked out before the service; testimonies such as we find in great biographies; each of these has its significant place in the worship service.

PLANNING THE SERVICE:—When a worship service for a group is arranged, usually a number of these elements are used together. Often an inexperienced leader or committee plans a service using a number of these elements in a hit or miss fashion. Some leaders are guided only by a sense of fitness or good taste in building the various elements into a service. There are, however, too many centuries of valuable Christian experience behind the public worship of the Church to decide the sequence of the elements merely on the basis of personal preference. Leaders and planning committees in church school and youth groups should be guided by some patterns of worship that have come out of the rich heritage and experience of the Church. Patterns of several such orders of worship may be found on pages 168 to 175 inclusive. The steps in the development of this order of worship might be used in building any worship service, namely, (a) A Vision of God; (b) Confession of Sin; (c) Assurance of Forgiveness; (d) A New Challenge or Sense of Missions; (e) A Rededication of Self.

The Church Year and the seasons suggest the use of various themes for worship services. However, even when a service of worship does not have a seasonal character it is valuable to select a dominant note in the Christian experience, or an aspect of the life of God, rather than to worship "in general". God is too great for our little minds to comprehend Him in all His greatness.— We need to be confronted in our group worship by various phases of His character and nature, such, for instance, as His power, His justice, and His love. The three complete worship services in this hymnal are examples of services with a dominant emphasis or theme.

Each Christian group should be building a library of worship materials— its own book of worship—adding to it year after year. Planning committees and leaders can then have available a rich and varied store of worship materials from which to make selection. The various sections of this hymnal on Calls to Worship, Prayers, Poetry, Responsive Readings, are to be thought of as beginnings for such a library of devotional literature.

Services of Worship
THE CHURCH

QUIET MUSIC "Hymn to Joy" (No. 19) Beethoven

OPENING SENTENCE

Power, and riches, and wisdom, and might, and honor, and glory, and blessing be unto our God forever and ever. Amen.

UNISON INVOCATION

O God, the source of all good gifts, we thank Thee for the rich heritage which is ours in Thy holy universal Church. Thou hast done much for us already and we believe that Thou hast much to give and teach us in our own time. Grant that Thy Church may never settle down to mere contentment with the tradition of the past. Grant that it may be alive to all new movements of Thy Spirit in the hearts and minds of men. May it stand always for the removal of injustice and the vindication of righteousness and truth; through Jesus Christ our Lord. Amen.

HYMN Tune: "Aurelia" (No. 82)

Thy hand, O God, has guided Thy Church from age to age:
The wondrous tale is written, Full clear, on every page;
Our fathers owned Thy goodness, And we Thy deeds record;
And both of this bear witness, One Church, one faith, one Lord.

Through many a day of darkness, Through many a scene of strife,
The faithful few fought bravely, To live the Christ-like life.
Their gospel was not weakness, But danger—life outpoured;
Their prayer, their hope, their victory, One Church, one faith, one Lord.

SCRIPTURE RECORDS FROM THE EARLY CHURCH

These that have turned the world upside down are come hither also.

But when her master saw that the hope of their gain was gone, they laid hold on Paul and Silas, and dragged them into the market place before the rulers, and when they had brought them unto the magistrates, they said, These men, being Jews, do exceedingly trouble our city, and set forth customs which it is not lawful for us to receive or to observe, being Romans.

And the multitude rose up together against them and the magistrates rent their garments off them and commanded to beat them with rods.

Festus saith with a loud voice, Paul, thou art mad; thy much learning is turning thee mad. But Paul saith, I am not mad, most excellent Festus; but speak forth words of truth and soberness. For the king knoweth of these things, unto whom also I speak freely; for I am persuaded that none of these things is hidden from him; for this hath not been done in a corner. King Agrippa, believest thou the prophets? I know that thou believest. And Agrippa said unto Paul, With but little persuasion thou wouldest fain make me a Christian. And Paul said, I would to God that whether with little or with much, not thou only, but also all that hear me this day, might become such as I am, except these bonds.

HYMN AND SCRIPTURE MEDITATION

Leader:—Now faith is the substance of things hoped for, the evidence of things not seen. For by it men of old obtained a good report.

Group:—(sings) (No. 134)
How firm a Foundation, ye saints of the Lord,
Is laid for your faith in His excellent word.
What more can He say than to you He hath said,
To you who for refuge to Jesus have fled?
To you who for refuge to Jesus have fled?

Leader:—The time will fail me if I tell of Gideon, Barak, Samson, Jephtha; of David and Samuel and the prophets who through faith subdued kingdoms, wrought righteousness, obtained promises, stopped the mouths of lions, quenched the power of fire, escaped the edge of the sword, from weakness were made strong, waxed mighty in war, turned to flight armies of aliens.

Group:—(sings)
When through fiery trials thy pathway shall lie,
My grace all sufficient shall be thy supply;
The flame shall not hurt thee; I only design
Thy dross to consume, and thy gold to refine;
Thy dross to consume, and thy gold to refine.

Leader:—They were stoned, they were sawn asunder, they were tempted, they were slain with the sword; they went about in sheepskins, in goatskins; being destitute, afflicted, ill-treated, wandering in deserts and mountains and caves and the holes of the earth.

Group:—(sings)
Fear not, I am with thee, O be not dismayed;
For I am thy God, And will still give thee aid;
I'll strengthen thee, help thee, and cause thee to stand,
Upheld by my righteous, omnipotent hand;
Upheld by my righteous, omnipotent hand.

Leader:—Therefore let us also, seeing we are compassed about with so great a cloud of witnesses, lay aside every weight, and the sin which doth so easily beset us, and let us run with patience the race that is set before us, looking unto Jesus the Author and Perfecter of our faith; who for the joy that was set before Him endured the cross, despising the shame, and hath set down at the right hand of the throne of God.

HYMN RESPONSE   No. 128 "Faith of Our Fathers"

Faith of our fathers, living still, In spite of dungeon, fire and sword,
O how our hearts beat high with joy, Whene'er we hear that glorious word!
Faith of our fathers, holy faith, We will be true to thee till death.

A GREAT "CHURCH" HYMN

"The Church's One Foundation"   Samuel J. Stone

Many times every year Christians repeat the words "I believe in the one Holy Universal Christian Church" or "I believe in the Holy Catholic Church". Dr. Samuel Stone, as a young Episcopalian minister was sent to serve a little mission chapel congregation composed mostly of people of the poorer classes and located on the outskirts of Windsor, England. He discovered that many of his parishioners were using the Creed in their prayers but they did not know what they prayed. To help them he wrote several hymns, each one explaining a phrase in the Creed. In this hymn the author tells of the divine origin of the Church in the first stanza; of its unbroken continuity down through the centuries, its unity and universality, in the second; its difficulties and final triumph in the third; and its communion with God and with the departed saints, in the fourth. The fact that this hymn is sung by Christians of almost every Protestant denomination around the world is probably due to the use of so many scriptural phrases in the hymn.₂

HYMN No. 82 "The Church's One Foundation"

"A PRAYER FOR THE CHURCH" OF TODAY   (Page 187) (Leader)

HYMN RESPONSE Tune "St. Catherine" (No. 128)

Our father's God from out whose hand, The centuries fall like grains of sand,
We thank Thee for the centuries gone, And trust Thee for the present one.
Oh, cast in some diviner mold, Let each new cycle shame the old. Amen.

SILENT BENEDICTION.

"LET JUSTICE ROLL DOWN AS WATERS"

QUIET MUSIC "Finlandia" (No. 81)   Jean Sibelius

A SILENT PRAYER

Christ, look upon us in this city, and keep our sympathy and pity
Fresh, and our faces heavenward, lest we grow hard.

CALL TO WORSHIP

Leader:—O God, Thy thoughts are not as our thoughts; nor Thy ways as our ways;
As high as the heavens are above the earth,
So high are Thy ways above our ways, and Thy thoughts above our thoughts.
People:—THOU ART HOLY, WE THY SINFUL CHILDREN CALL UPON THEE.

HYMN Tune: "Lancashire (No. 65)

O God of earth and altar, Bow down and hear our cry;
Our earthly rulers falter, Our people drift and die;
The walls of gold entomb us, The swords of scorn divide;
Take not Thy thunder from us, But take away our pride. Amen.

VOICES FROM THE SCRIPTURES   (To be read by individuals)

The Psalmist speaks:—Help Lord; for the godly man ceaseth; for the faithful fail from among the children of men.
We know not, neither do we understand, we walk on in darkness, all the foundations of the earth are out of course.
Consider and hear me, O Lord, my God, lighten my eyes, lest I sleep the sleep of death.

The Prophet speaks:—Thus saith the Lord:
> These people choose their own ways
> And delight in their abomination;
> So will I also choose the outrages they are to endure,
> And will bring upon them the terrors they dread;
> Because, when I called, no one answered,
> When I spoke, they did not listen;
> But they did what was evil in my eyes,
> And chose what displeased me.

Jesus speaks:—O Jerusalem, Jerusalem, that killeth the prophets, and stoneth them that are sent unto her: How often would I have gathered thy children together, even as a hen gathereth her chickens under her wings, and ye would not!

And when He drew nigh, He saw the city and wept over it . . .

MEDITATION "Christ Mourns Over the City" Artist: Paul Flandrin (Leader)

Christ stands on Olivet and with the vision of a Seer looks down the vistas of time. Jerusalem lying before Him is dissolved in the mist, and in its stead He sees the modern city with compact tiers of tenements. Behind where the temple of the living God once stood, there is murky smoke and reeking steam and through the gloom come the pulse beats of trip hammers and sudden spurts of white hot flames from furnace doors. Some new god is being worshipped here. You can see the hosts assembling to serve him. Many little children are driving their tasks from dawn till sunset amid the rattle and roar of looms and gears.

Above we see the domes and towers of great cathedrals, but they stand deserted. If there is organ music rolling through the lofty aisles no ear hears it. There may be priests at the altar, but the people are not thronging thither for the bread of life, they are tending their fires and their hammers, they are fighting for the bread that perishes; they are hating one another in their greed.

The Seer stands motionless above the city, His hands clasped in contemplation, His sad yet fascinated face still gazing on the sights and sounds that strike upon His soul. Where are His disciples? Have they given up in despair the preaching of love and goodwill? Is there no way to say, "see that ye despise not these little ones", no one to throw down the altars that smoke to mammon; no one to repeat the old commandment, "Thou shalt worship the Lord Thy God and Him only shalt thou serve;" and the one like unto it, "Thou shalt love thy neighbor as thyself"?

After nineteen centuries, millions of our fellows are unemployed and supported by charity; the majority, even in prosperous times dwell in poverty, while the wealth of the world is controlled by a few. We live in a social order that sets every man's hand against his brother; hatreds of race and nation and class divide us.

Let us pray.

A LITANY FOR DELIVERANCE

God have mercy upon us miserable sinners.
> GOD HAVE MERCY UPON US MISERABLE SINNERS.

For our ignorance and our greed which have brought to multitudes starvation in the midst of plenty,
> LORD, HAVE MERCY UPON US.

From a sense of our own virtue at some slight charity to the unemployed,
> GOOD LORD, DELIVER US.

From heedless comfort in the security of our homes, while families of the poor are evicted from the tenements, their children and furniture upon the street,

GOOD LORD, DELIVER US.

From spending billions for battleships while the unemployed live upon a crust,

GOOD LORD, DELIVER US.

From methods of private or public relief which save the bodies of men but destroy their inmost spirit; from hurting the finer sensibilities of men and women, robbing them of their pride and self-respect,

GOOD LORD, DELIVER US.

From false notions that by preaching we can save the souls of men, while unemployment breaks their hearts, unbalances their minds, destroys their homes, tempts them beyond measure, visits want and disease upon their children; turns the heart to bitterness, hatred and rebellion, or to hopelessness, despair and death,

GOOD LORD, DELIVER US.

From ever forgetting the forlorn figure of the unemployed; from failure to see that our social fabric is as shabby as his coat, and that our heads must bow in equal shame with his,

GOOD LORD, DELIVER US.

From satisfaction with any revivial of trade or renewed prosperity while multitudes still can find no work,

GOOD LORD, DELIVER US.

That our conscience may know no rest until unemployment is abolished,

WE BESEECH THEE TO HEAR US, GOOD LORD.

That it may please Thee to guide us into the good life in which there shall be peace and plenty; a sharing of labor and leisure and joy by all the children of men,

WE BESEECH THEE TO HEAR US, GOOD LORD. AMEN.

HYMN   No. 176 "When Wilt Thou Save the People?"

THE NEW CITY   (Leader)

And I saw the Holy City, the new Jerusalem, coming down out of heaven from God. I saw a new heaven and a new earth, for the first heaven and the first earth are passed away. And I heard a great voice out of heaven saying: Behold, the tabernacle of God is with men, and He shall dwell with them, and He shall be their God, and they shall be His people. Behold! God maketh all things new.

> Have we seen her, O my brothers,
> The New City, where each hour
> Is a poet's revelation, or a hero's perfect power,
> Have we seen her, the New City,
> In her glory — ah, not yet —
> But her site is surely purchased
> And her pattern is designed,
> And her blessed ways are visions
> For all striving humankind.
> Let our lives be in the building
> We shall lay us in the sod
> Happier, if our human travail
> Builds her avenues toward God.

HYMN   No. 144 "We Would Be Building"

SILENT BENEDICTION

Christ, look upon us in this city, and keep our sympathy and pity Fresh, and our faces heavenward, lest we grow hard.

INSTRUMENTAL AMEN.

A SERVICE OF CONSECRATION AND DEDICATION

(Based upon the worship experience of Isaiah, as a young man, in the temple)

QUIET MUSIC "Sanctus" From "The Holy City" (No. 206) Gaul
Be still, and know that I am God.

A VISION OF GOD (Leader)
In the year that King Uzziah died I saw the Lord sitting upon a throne, high and lifted up, and His train filled the temple.

HYMN OF PRAISE No. 20 "Praise The Lord, Ye Heavens Adore Him"

A VISION OF THE HOLY GOD
And one (of the seraphim) cried unto another, and said, Holy, Holy, Holy, is the Lord of Hosts — the whole earth is full of His glory.

RESPONSE Tune: "Chautauqua" (No. 8) Chorus (Sung by the worshipers)
Holy, Holy, Holy, Lord God of Hosts,
Heaven and earth are full of Thee,
Heaven and earth are praising Thee,
O Lord, most high. Amen.

CONFESSION OF SIN (Leader)
Then said I, woe is me: for I am undone: Because I am a man of unclean lips, and I dwell in the midst of a people of unclean lips—for mine eyes have seen the King, the Lord of Hosts.
*
**

UNISON PRAYER
O God, we confess the sorry confusion of our common life,
In Thy presence our disguises and pretenses do not avail.
In the light of Thy holiness we know ourselves for what we are.
We acknowledge that the world's sin is our own,
That the greed which we condemn in others, is in our own hearts.
That the world is unjust because none of us love justice with sufficient abandon.
Give us grace to look into our hearts before we cast a stone of condemnation.
May we achieve the grace of true humility in Thy presence so that we may cease to defeat Thy will for the world, by our own self-will.
May the vision of what we might be convict us of what we are so that Thy mercy may redeem us of our sin through Jesus Christ our Lord. Amen.

ANTIPHONAL HYMN Tune: "Bullinger" (No. 161)
Solo—Art thou weary, heavy laden, art thou sore distrest?
"Come to Me", said One, "And, coming, be at rest."
Group—Hath He marks to lead me to Him, if He be my Guide?
Solo—In His feet and hands are wound-prints, and His side.
Group—If I ask Him to receive me, will He say me nay?
Solo—Not till earth and not till heaven pass away.
Group—Finding, following, keeping, struggling, is He sure to bless?
Solo—Saints, apostles, prophets, martyrs, answer, "Yes".

PROMISE OF PARDON (Leader)

If my people, which are called by name, shall humble themselves, and pray and seek my face, and turn them from their wicked ways—then shall I hear their prayer and will forgive their sins and heal them, saith the Lord . . . I will be their God and they shall be my people.

ASSURANCE OF FORGIVENESS (Leader)

Then flew one of the seraphim unto me, having a live coal in his hand which he had taken with the tongs from off the altar. And touched my mouth with it and said, Lo, this hath touched thy lips; and thine iniquity is taken away, and thy sin forgiven.

HYMN RESPONSE

My faith looks up to Thee, Thou Lamb of Calvary, Saviour Divine. Now hear me while I pray, Take all my guilt away, O let me from this day, Be wholly Thine.
***

THE CALL (Leader)

And I heard the voice of the Lord, saying, Whom shall I send, and who will go for us?

HYMN Tune: "Lancashire" (No. 65)

Group:
The voice of God is calling its summons unto men
As once He spake in Zion, so now He speaks again.
Whom shall I send to succor my people in their need?
Whom shall I send to loosen the bonds of shame and greed?

Solo:
I hear my people crying in cot and mine and slum
No field or mart is silent, no city street is dumb.
I see my people falling in darkness and despair.
Whom shall I send to shatter the fetters which they bear?

THE ANSWER

Then said I, Here am I, send me.
****

HYMN (continued)

Group:
We heed, O Lord, Thy summons, and answer, Here are we:
Send us upon Thine errand, Let us Thy servants be.
Our strength is dust and ashes, our years a passing hour
But thou canst use our weakness to magnify Thy power.
From ease and plenty save us, from price of place absolve,
Purge us of low desire, lift us to high resolve.
Take us, and make us holy, teach us Thy will and way.
Speak, and, behold, we answer, Command, and we obey.

THE COMMISSION (Leader)

And He said, Go, and tell this people . . .

WORDS OF JESUS (To be read silently by each worshiper as the pianist plays quietly "O Jesus I Have Promised" No. 150 one stanza)

And He called unto Him the multitude with His disciples, and said unto them, If any man would come after me, let him deny himself, and take up his cross, and follow me, For whosoever would save his life shall lose it; and whosoever shall lose his life for my sake and the Gospel's shall save it. For what doth it profit a man, to gain the whole world, and forfeit his life?

   *   *In a service of greater length the Negro spiritual "Were You There When They Crucified My Lord" might be sung here by a solo voice or a group of voices.*

   **   *After the singing of the spiritual, the poem "Jesus of Nazareth" by Ernest Cadman Colwell, Christendom, Spring, 1936 — quoted in "Living Courageously", Kirby Page, page 306, may be read.*

   ***   *To express the note of exultation following the assurance of forgiveness Mendelssohn's "Lift Thine Eyes, O Lift Thine Eyes" could be used instrumentally or sung by several voices.*

   *****If this service is used as a consecration service for teachers or youth cabinets or on similar occasions the service of dedication given below, or another one typed and given to the teachers or officers could be introduced. Those being commissioned would come to the front during the singing of the previous hymn. They would join in the words "Then said I, Here am I, send me:" and the dedication litany, and if the group is large enough they could sing the two concluding stanzas of the hymn.*

A DEDICATION FOR CHURCH SCHOOL TEACHERS

Minister:—For the holy privilege of being teachers, chosen representatives of the Great Teacher Himself, and of sharing in the wonder and discovery, the pain and the ecstacy of growing life—

Teachers:—Our gratitude to Thee, Oh Lord, and Thy blessing upon those we teach, and upon us.

Minister:—For the eager responsiveness of childhood, for the daring and the dreams of youth, for the might and wisdom of growing manhood, these priceless human resources with which we work—

Teachers:—Our gratitude to Thee, Oh Lord, and Thy blessing upon those we teach, and upon us.

Minister:—For the resources of Thy Spirit whereby we become laborers together with God—

Teachers:—Our gratitude to Thee, Oh Lord, and Thy blessing upon those we teach, and upon us.

Minister:—For a more Christlike understanding of those whom we teach, for insight to sense their inward selves, for patience to await the full fruitage of truth in their lives, for wisdom in understanding the paths which Thy feet follow in the full redemption of growing life—

Teachers:—We earnestly beseech Thee, Oh Lord.

Minister:—To the fulfillment of the sacred office of teaching and the discharge of its full responsibilities—

Teachers:—We dedicate to the utmost the powers of our hands, our minds, and our inmost selves in the spirit and presence of Christ.₈

Opening Sentences

1. Make a joyful noise unto the Lord; all ye lands.
   Serve the Lord with gladness; come before His presence with singing.

2. O come, let us worship and bow down; let us kneel before the Lord our Maker.

3. I will lift up mine eyes unto the hills, from whence cometh my help.
   My help cometh from the Lord, which made heaven and earth.

4. O Lord, open thou my lips;
   And my mouth shall shew forth Thy praise

5. The Lord is in His holy temple,
   Let all the earth keep silence before Him.

6. Seek ye the Lord while He may be found, call ye upon Him while He is near.

7. Praise waiteth for Thee, O God, in Zion; And unto Thee shall the vow be performed
   O Thou that hearest prayer, unto Thee shall all flesh come.

8. The Lord is my light and my salvation; whom shall I fear?
   The Lord is the strength of my life; of whom shall I be afraid?

9. One thing have I desired of the Lord, that will I seek after;
   That I may dwell in the house of the Lord all the days of my life,
   To behold the beauty of the Lord and to enquire in His temple.

10. Who shall ascend into the hill of the Lord? or who shall stand in His holy place?
    He that hath clean hands, and a pure heart; who hath not lifted up his soul unto vanity, nor sworn deceitfully.

Offertory Sentences

1. Remember the words of the Lord Jesus, how He said, It is more blessed to give than to receive.

2. He which soweth sparingly shall reap also sparingly; and he which soweth bountifully shall reap also bountifully.

3. To do good and to communicate forget not; for with such sacrifices God is well pleased.

4. Every man according as he purposeth in his heart so let him give; not grudgingly, or of necessity; for God loveth a cheerful giver.

5. Whoso hath this world's good, and seeth his brother have need, and shutteth up his compassion from him, how dwelleth the love of God in him?

Closing Prayers

1. May the peace of God which passeth all understanding keep our hearts and minds, through Christ Jesus. Amen.

2. The Lord watch between me and thee, when we are absent one from another.

Classified Scripture References for Responsive Readings

CHURCH YEAR SEASONS

GENERAL WORSHIP: Psalm 84

ADVENT: Season of Expectancy
Isaiah 11:1-9, 40:1-11

CHRISTMASTIDE: Season of the
Nativity
Isaiah 9:2-7
Luke 2:1-20

EPIPHANY: Season of the Evangel
and Missions
Psalm 8:
Psalm 46:
Matthew 28:16-20
Acts 17:22-31

LENT: Season of Renewal
Psalm 51:1-17
Psalm 130:
Isaiah 1:10-20

PALM SUNDAY: Psalm 24:
Isaiah 61:1-6

GOOD FRIDAY: Isaiah 53:1-6, 10-12

EASTERTIDE: Season of the Resurrection

Psalm 146
Philippians 2:1-11

WHITSUNDAY: Season of the Baptism
of the Holy Spirit
Acts 2:1-4, 14-18

KINGDOMTIDE: Trinity Season of the
Church and Kingdom Loyalties

THE GREATNESS OF GOD:
Psalm 19
Psalm 67

THE GOODNESS OF GOD:
Psalm 23
John 14:1-14

THE CHRISTIAN LIFE:
John 15:1-14
Ephesians 6:10-20

THE BIBLE:
Psalm 119:1-16

THE CHURCH:
Ephesians 4:1-7, 11-13

THE KINGDOM:
Revelation 21:1-7.

SPECIAL DAYS

CONFIRMATION DAY:
Psalm 27

The Lord is my light and my salvation;
Whom shall I fear?

**The Lord is the strength of my life;
Of whom shall I be afraid?**

When evil-doers came upon me to eat
up my flesh,
Even mine adversaries and my foes, they
stumbled and fell.

**Though a host should encamp against me,
My heart shall not fear;
Though war should rise against me,
Even then will I be confident.**

One thing have I asked of the Lord,
that will I seek after:
That I may dwell in the house of the
Lord all the days of my life,

**To behold the beauty of the Lord,
And to inquire in His temple.**

For in the day of trouble He will keep
me secretly in His pavilion:

**In the covert of His tabernacle will He
hide me;
He will lift me up upon a rock.**

And now shall my head be lifted up
above mine enemies round about me;
And I will offer in His tabernacle sacrifices of joy;

**I will sing, yea, I will sing praises unto the
Lord.**

Hear, O Lord, when I cry with my voice:
Have mercy also upon me, and answer
me.

**When Thou saidst, Seek ye my face; my
heart said unto Thee,
Thy face, Lord, will I seek.**

Hide not thy face from me;
Put not Thy servant away in anger:
Thou hast been my help;
Cast me not off, neither forsake me, O
God of my salvation.

**When my father and my mother forsake
me,**

Then the Lord will take me up.

Teach me thy way, O Lord; And lead me in a plain path, Because of mine enemies.

Deliver me not over unto the will of mine adversaries:

For false witnesses are risen up against me, And such as breathe out cruelty.

I had fainted, unless I had believed to see the goodness of the Lord In the land of the living.

Wait for the Lord;

Be strong, and let thy heart take courage; Yea, wait thou for the Lord.

REFORMATION DAY:

Romans 5:1-11

Being therefore justified by faith, we have peace with God through our Lord Jesus Christ;

Through whom also we have had our access by faith into this grace wherein we stand; and we rejoice in hope of the glory of God.

And not only so, but we also rejoice in our tribulations: knowing that tribulation worketh steadfastness;

And stedfastness, approvedness; and approvedness, hope:

And hope putteth not to shame; because the love of God hath been shed abroad in our hearts through the Holy Spirit which was given unto us.

For while we were yet weak, in due season Christ died for the ungodly.

For scarcely for a righteous man will one die: for peradventure for the good man some one would even dare to die.

But God commendeth His own love toward us, in that, while we were yet sinners, Christ died for us.

Much more then, being now justified by His blood, shall we be saved from the wrath of God through Him.

For if, while we were enemies, we were reconciled to God through the death of His Son, much more, being reconciled, shall we be saved by His life;

And not only so, but we also rejoice in God through our Lord Jesus Christ, through whom we have now received the reconciliation.

EDUCATION DAY:

Proverbs 3:13-26

Happy is the man that findeth wisdom, And the man that getting understanding.

For the gaining of it is better than the gaining of silver,

And the profit thereof than fine gold.

She is more precious than rubies:

And none of the things thou canst desire are to be compared unto her.

Length of days is in her right hand;

In her left hand are riches and honor.

Her ways are ways of pleasantness, And all her paths are peace.

She is a tree of life to them that lay hold upon her:

And happy is every one that retaineth her.

The Lord by wisdom founded the earth;

By understanding he established the heavens.

By His knowledge the depths were broken up,

And the skies drop down the dew.

My son, let them not depart from thine eyes;

Keep sound wisdom and discretion:

So shall they be life unto thy soul, And grace to thy neck.

Then shalt thou walk in thy way securely,

And thy foot shall not stumble.

When thou liest down, thou shalt not be afraid:

Yea, thou shalt lie down and thy sleep shall be sweet.

Be not afraid of sudden fear, Neither of the desolation of the wicked, when it cometh:

For the Lord will be thy confidence, And will keep thy foot from being taken.

RALLY DAY:

Matthew 18:1-6

In that hour came the disciples unto Jesus, saying, Who then is greatest in the Kingdom of heaven?

And He called to Him a little child, and set him in the midst of them, and said,

Verily I say unto you, Except ye turn, and become as little children, ye shall in no wise enter into the kingdom of heaven.

Whosoever therefore shall humble himself as this little child, the same is the greatest in the kingdom of heaven.

And whoso shall receive one such little child in my name receiveth me:

But whoso shall cause one of these little ones that believe on me to stumble, it is profitable for him that a great millstone should be hanged about his neck, and that he should be sunk in the depth of the sea.

THANKSGIVING DAY:

Psalm 103

Bless the Lord, O my soul;
And all that is within me, bless His holy name.

Bless the Lord, O my soul, And forget not all His benefits;

Who forgiveth all thine iniquities;
Who healeth all thy diseases;

Who redeemeth thy life from destruction;
Who crowneth thee with lovingkindness and tender mercies;

Who satisfieth thy desire with good things,
So that thy youth is renewed like the eagle.

The Lord executeth righteous acts,
And judgments for all that are oppressed.

He made known His ways unto Moses,
His doings unto the children of Israel.

The Lord is merciful and gracious,
Slow to anger, and abundant in loving-kindness.

He will not always chide;
Neither will He keep His anger for ever.

He hath not dealt with us after our sins,
Nor rewarded us after our iniquities.

For as the heavens are high above the earth,
So great is His lovingkindness toward them that fear Him.

As far as the east is from the west,
So far hath He removed our transgressions from us.

Like as a father pitieth his children,
So the Lord pitieth them that fear Him.

For He knoweth our frame;
He remembereth that we are dust.

As for man, his days are as grass;
As a flower of the field, so he flourisheth.

For the wind passeth over it, and it is gone;
And the place thereof shall know it no more.

But the lovingkindness of the Lord is from everlasting to everlasting upon them that fear Him.

And His righteousness unto children's children;

To such as keep His covenant,
And to those that remember His precepts to do them.

The Lord hath established His throne in the heavens;
And His kingdom ruleth over all.

Bless the Lord, ye His angels,
That are mighty in strength, that fulfill His word,
Hearkening unto the voice of His word.

Bless the Lord, all ye His hosts,
Ye ministers of His, that do His pleasure.

Bless the Lord, all ye His works,
In all places of His dominion:
Bless the Lord, O my soul.

MOTHERS' DAY:

I Corinthians 13

If I speak with the tongues of men and of angels, but have not love, I am become sounding brass, or a clanging cymbal.

And if I have the gift of prophecy, and know all mysteries and all knowledge; and if I have all faith, so as to remove mountains, but have not love, I am nothing.

And if I bestow all my goods to feed the poor, and if I give my body to be burned, but have not love, it profiteth me nothing.

Love suffereth long, and is kind; love envieth not; love vaunteth not itself, is not puffed up,

Doth not behave itself unseemly, seeketh not its own, is not provoked, taketh not account of evil;

Rejoiceth not in unrighteousness, but rejoiceth with the truth;

Beareth all things, believeth all things, hopeth all things, endureth all things.

Love never faileth: but whether there be prophecies, they shall be done away; whether there be tongues, they shall cease; whether there be knowledge, it shall be done away.

For we know in part, and we prophesy in part;

But when that which is perfect is come, that which is in part shall be done away.

When I was a child, I spake as a child, I felt as a child, I thought as a child; now that I am become a man, I have put away childish things.

For now we see in a mirror, darkly; but then face to face:

Now I know in part; but then shall I know fully even as also I was fully known.

But now abideth faith, hope, love, these three; and the greatest of these is love.

PATRIOTIC DAYS:

Psalm 33:1-12

Rejoice in the Lord, O ye righteous: Praise is comely for the upright.

Give thanks unto the Lord with the harp: Sing praises unto Him with the psaltery of ten strings.

Sing unto Him a new song; Play skilfully with a loud noise.

For the word of the Lord is right; And all his work is done in faithfulness.

He loveth righteousness and justice: The earth is full of the lovingkindness of the Lord.

By the word of the Lord were the heavens made, And all the host of them by the breath of His mouth.

He gathereth the waters of the sea together as a heap: He layeth up the deeps in storehouses.

Let all the earth fear the Lord: Let all the inhabitants of the world stand in awe of Him.

For He spake, and it was done; He commanded, and it stood fast.

The Lord bringeth the counsel of the nations to nought; He maketh the thoughts of the peoples to be of no effect.

The counsel of the Lord standeth fast for ever, The thoughts of His heart to all generations.

Blessed is the nation whose God is the Lord, The people whom He hath chosen for His own inheritance.

Micah 4:1-5

But in the latter days it shall come to pass, that the mountain of the Lord's house shall be established on the top of the mountains, and it shall be exalted above the hills; and peoples shall flow unto it.

And many nations shall go and say, Come ye, and let us go up to the mountain of the Lord, and to the house of the God of Jacob;

And He will teach us of His ways, and we will walk in His paths. For out of Zion shall go forth the law, and the word of the Lord from Jerusalem;

And He will judge between many peoples, and will decide concerning strong nations afar off:

And they shall beat their swords into plowshares, and their spears into pruning-hooks; nation shall not lift up sword against nation, neither shall they learn war any more.

But they shall sit every man under his vine and under his fig-tree; and none shall make them afraid: for the mouth of the Lord of Hosts hath spoken it.

For all the peoples walk every one in the name of his God; and we will walk in the name of the Lord our God for ever and ever.

Devotional Poetry and Prose

(Choice devotional selections which may often be used to enrich the service of worship)

•

MORNING AND EVENING WORSHIP

•

Look to This Day

Look to this day!
For it is life, the very life of life.
In its brief course lie all the varieties
and realities of your existence:
The bliss of growth;
The glory of action;
The splendor of beauty;
For yesterday is already a dream, and
tomorrow is only a vision;
But today, well lived, makes every yes-
terday
A dream of happiness, and every to-
morrow a vision of hope.
Look well, therefore, to this day!
Such is the salutation of the dawn!。

The Day

The day will bring some lovely thing,
I say it over each new dawn;
"Some gay, adventurous thing to hold
Against my heart, when it is gone."
And so I rise and go to meet
The day with wings upon my feet.
I come upon it unaware—
Some sudden beauty without name;
A snatch of song, a breath of pine;
A poem lit with golden flame;
High tangled bird notes, keenly thinned,
Like flying color on the wing.

No day has ever failed me quite—
Before the grayest day is done,
I come upon some misty bloom
Or a late line of crimson sun.
Each night I pause, remembering
Some gay, adventurous, lovely thing.。

The One Thousandth Psalm

O God, we thank Thee for everything!
For the sea and its waves, blue, green
and gray and always wonderful;
For the beach and the breakers and the
spray and the white foam on the rocks;
For the blue arch of heaven; for the
clouds in the sky, white and gray and
purple;
For the green of the grass; for the
forests in their spring beauty; for the
wheat and corn and rye and barley.
For the brown earth turned up by the
plow, for the sun by day, and the
dews by night;
We thank Thee for all Thou hast made
and that Thou hast called it good.
For all the glory and beauty and wonder
of the world;
For the glory of springtime, the tints of
the flowers and their fragrance;
For the glory of the summer flowers,
the roses and cardinals and clethra;
For the glory of the autumn, the scarlet
and crimson and gold of the forest;
For the glory of winter, the pure snow
on the shrubs and trees.
We thank Thee that Thou hast placed
us in the world to subdue all things
to Thy glory,
And to use all things for the good of
Thy children.
We thank Thee! We enter into Thy
work, and go about Thy business.。

Nature's Creed

I believe in the brook as it wanders
From hillside into glade;
I believe in the breeze as it whispers
When evening's shadows fade.
I believe in the roar of the river
As it dashes from high cascade;
I believe in the cry of the tempest
'Mid the thunder's cannonade.
I believe in the light of shining stars,
I believe in the sun and the moon;
I believe in the flash of lightning,
I believe in the nightbird's croon.
I believe in the faith of the flowers,
I believe in the rock and the sod,
For in all of these appeareth clear
The handiwork of God.

Flower in the Crannied Wall

Flower in the crannied wall,
I pluck you out of the crannies;—
Hold you here, root and all, in my hand,
Little flower—but if I could understand

What you are, root and all, and all in all,
I should know what God and man is.[12]
Earth's crammed with heaven,
And every common bush afire with
God.[13]

The Sky-Born Music

Let me go where'er I will
I hear a sky-born music still;
It sounds from all things old,
It sounds from all things young,
From all that's fair, from all that's foul
Peals out a cheerful song.
It is not only in the rose,
It is not only in the bird,
Not only when the rainbow glows,
Nor in the song of women heard,
But in the darkest meanest things
There alway, alway, something sings.
'Tis not in the high stars alone,
Not in the cups of budding flowers,
Nor in the redbreast's mellow tones,
Nor in the bow that smiles in showers,
But in the mud and scum of things
There alway, alway, something sings.[14]

LIFE AND WORK OF JESUS

Our Christ

I know not how that Bethlehem's Babe
Could in the God-head be;
I only know the Manger Child
Has brought God's life to me.
I know not how that Calvary's cross
A world from sin could free:
I only know its matchless love
Has brought God's love to me.
I know not how that Joseph's tomb
Could solve death's mystery:
I only know a living Christ,
Our immortality.[15]

Song of Christian Workingmen

Our Master toiled, a carpenter
Of busy Galilee;
He knew the weight of ardent tasks
And ofttimes, wearily,
He sought, apart, in earnest prayer
For strength, beneath His load of care.
He took a manly share of work,
No thoughtless shirker He.
From dawn to dusk, before His bench,
He labored faithfully.
He felt just pride in work well done
And found rest sweet, at setting sun.

His Father worked, and He rejoiced
That honest toil was His—
To whom was given grace to know
Divinest mysteries:
And shall not we find toiling good
Who serve in labor's brotherhood?[16]

Jesus the Carpenter

If I could hold within my hand
The hammer Jesus swung,
Not all the gold in all the land,
Nor jewels countless as the sand,
All in the balance flung,
Could weigh the value of that thing
Round which His fingers once did cling.
If I could have the table Christ
Once made in Nazareth,
Not all the pearls in all the sea,
Nor crowns of kings or kings to be
As long as men have breath,
Could buy that thing of wood He made—
The Lord of Lords who learned a trade.
Yea, but His hammer still is shown
By honest hands that toil
And round His table men sit down;
And all are equals, with a crown
Nor gold nor pearls can soil;
The shop of Nazareth was bare—
But brotherhood was builded there.[17]

THE BIBLE

We search the world for truth. We cull
The good, the true, the beautiful,
From graven stone and written scroll,
And all old flower-fields of the soul;
And, weary seekers of the best,
We come back laden from our quest,
To find that all the sages said
Is in the Book our mothers read.[18]

THE CHURCH

This is the Church of my dreams.
A Church adequate for the task.
The Church of the warm heart,
Of the open mind,
Of the adventurous spirit;
The Church that cares,
That heals hurt lives,
That comforts old people,
That challenges youth;
That knows no divisions of culture or
class,
No frontiers, geographical or social,
The Church that inquires as well as
avers,

That looks forward as well as backward,
The Church of the Master,
The Church of the people,
The high Church, the broad Church, the low Church,
—High as the ideals of Jesus,
—Low as the humblest human;
A working Church,
A worshipping Church,
A winsome Church;
A Church that interprets the truth in terms of truth
That inspires courage for this life and hope for the life to come;
A Church of all good men,
The Church of the living God.[19]

God's Temples

I so love little Churches!
Vine-clad, of stone or brick,
Hid among elms and birches,
Time-hallowed, gentle places,
With welcome that embraces
Both saint and heretic.
Blest are the country Churches!
I love their simple ways,
Their heartfelt hymns that clearly
Soar up to God sincerely;
My heart remembers dearly
Those bygone Sabbath days.
I sought God in cathedrals
Vast aisles of white and gold;
Where waves of glorious music
From the great organ rolled.
But God seemed high in heaven.
I could not sense Him there;
In all that pomp and glory
There seemed no room for prayer.
Ah, give me little Churches
My happy childhood knew!
Time-hallowed, gentle places,
Hid among elms and birches
Dear little country Churches—
I think God loves them, too![20]

PRAYER AND THE INNER LIFE

Sanctuary

Let us put by some hour of every day
For holy things!—whether it be when dawn
Peers through the window pane, or when the noon
Flames, like a burnished topaz, in the vault,
Or when the thrush pours in the ear of eve

Its plaintive monody; some little hour
Wherein to hold rapt converse with the soul,
From sordidness and self a sanctuary,
Swept by the winnowing of unseen wings,
And touched by the White Light Ineffable![21]

The Larger Prayer

At first I prayed for Light:
  Could I but see the way,
How gladly, swiftly would I walk
  To everlasting day.
And next I prayed for Strength:
  That I might tread the road
With firm, unfaltering feet and win
  The heaven's serene abode.
And then I asked for Faith:
  Could I but trust my God
I'd live enfolded in His peace.
  Though foes were all abroad.
But now I pray for Love:
  Deep love to God and man,
A living love that will not fail,
  However dark his plan.
And Light and Strength and Faith
  Are opening everywhere;
God only waited for me, till
  I prayed the larger prayer.[22]

We Thank Thee, Lord

We Thank Thee, Lord,
For all Thy Golden Silences—
Silence of moorlands rolling to the skies,
Heath-purpled, bracken-clad, aflame with gorse;
Silence of deep woods' mystic cloistered calm;
Silence of wide seas basking in the sun;
Silence of white peaks soaring to the blue;
Silence of dawnings, when, their matins sung,
The little birds do fall asleep again;
For the deep silence of the golden noons;
Silence of gloamings and the setting sun;
Silence of moonlit nights and patterned glades;
Silence of stars, magnificently still,
Yet ever chanting their Creator's skill;
Deep unto deep, within us sound sweet chords
Of praise beyond the reach of human words;
In our souls' silence, feeling only Thee—
  We thank Thee, thank Thee,
  Thank Thee Lord![23]

Ultima Veritas

In the bitter waves of woe
  Beaten and tossed about
By the sullen winds that blow
  From the desolate shores of doubt—
When the anchors that faith had cast
  Are dragging in the gale,
I am quietly holding fast
  To the things that cannot fail:
I know that right is right;
  That it is not good to lie;
That love is better than spite,
  And a neighbor than a spy;
I know that passion needs
  The leash of a sober mind;
I know that generous deeds
  Some sure reward will find;
That the rulers must obey;
  That the givers shall increase;
That duty lights the way
  For the beautiful feet of Peace;—
In the darkest night of the year,
  When the stars have all gone out,
That courage is better than fear,
  That faith is truer than doubt;
And fierce though the fiends may fight,
  And long though the angels hide,
I know that Truth and Right
  Have the universe on their side;
And that somewhere, beyond the stars,
  Is a Love that is better than fate;
When the night unlocks her bars
  I shall see Him, and I will wait.[24]

A Boy's Prayer

Give me clean hands, clean words, and clean thoughts; help me to stand for the hard right against the easy wrong; save me from habits that harm; teach me to work as hard and play as fair in Thy sight alone as if all the world saw; forgive me when I am unkind; and help me to forgive those who are unkind to me; keep me ready to help others at some cost to myself; send me chances to do a little good every day, and to grow more like Christ. Amen.[25]

A Teacher's Prayer

As from this consecrated hour,
  O Lord, I onward press,
Thy deep o'er-brooding spirit lend
  To steel my feebleness!
'Tis only strength I ask of Thee,
  To lead the minds aright
Of those whom Thou hast sent to me:

O Lord, anoint my sight.
As Sabbath bells call open hearts
  Thy living way to know;
Grant me a never-tiring zeal,
  My best, Lord, to bestow.
Let clear and high my witness stand;
  Keep me a learner till
With fuller faith I understand
  And teach Thy holy will.[26]

In Thy Presence

Lord, what a change within us one short hour
Spent in Thy presence will prevail to make!
What heavy burdens from our bosoms take,
What parched grounds refresh as with a shower!
We kneel, and all around us seems to lower;
We rise, and all, the distant and the near,
Stands forth in sunny outline brave and clear;
We kneel, how weak; we rise, how full of power![27]

COURAGE, FAITH, LOYALTY

The Lure of the Unattained

It is easy to foot the trodden path
Where thousands walked before.
It is simple to push my fragile bark
Past reefs of a charted shore.
I find it good to ride the road
Where others laid the rail.
It is well to test the ocean's strength
Where others also sail.
But when a dream enslaves a man,
A dream of the vast untrod,
A dream that says, "Strike out with me,
Strike out or part with God."
A dream that leads to an untried path
Where unknown tempests blow.
And the only chart a man can boast
Is his will that bids him go.
Ah, then, my soul bethink yourself,
For God has spread this scroll
To test the stuff of your rough-hewn faith
And the fibre of your soul.[28]

CONSECRATION

Jesus Christ—and We

Christ has no hands but our hands
  To do His work today;
He has no feet but our feet
  To lead men in His way;
He has no tongue but our tongues
  To tell men how He died;
He has no help but our help
  To bring them to His side.
What if our hands are busy
  With other work than His?
What if our feet are walking
  Where sin's allurement is?
What if our tongues are speaking
  Of things His lips would spurn?
How can we hope to help Him
  Unless from Him we learn?[29]

From the Vision of Sir Launfal

The holy supper is kept, indeed,
In whatso we share with another's need;
Not that which we give, but what we
  share,
For the gift without the giver is bare;
Who bestows himself with his alms feeds
  three—
Himself, his hungering neighbor, and
  Me.[30]

THE NATION AND WORLD FRIENDSHIP

The Fatherland

Where is the true man's fatherland?
  Is it where he by chance is born?
Doth not the yearning spirit scorn
  In such scant borders to be spanned?
Oh, yes! his fatherland must be
As the blue heavens, wide and free!
Is it alone where freedom is?
  Where God is God and man is man?
Doth he not claim a broader span
  For the soul's love of home than this?
Oh, yes! his fatherland must be
As the blue heavens, wide and free!
Where'er a human heart doth wear
  Joy's myrtle-wreath or sorrows gyves,
Where'er a human spirit strives
After a life more true and fair.
There is the true man's birthplace grand,
His is a world-wide fatherland![31]

The Tried and the Untried

The Tried

To build a world of brotherhood by the
  machinery of war;
To establish fellowship by feeding racial
  rancor — by keeping the Negro and
  immigrant in place;
To use force and violence in guarantee-
  ing national security;
To dispose of the criminal by a prison
  system;
To put money first in the purpose of
  life;
                and
To be a Christian without following
  Christ.

The Untried

To build a friendly world by faith and
  understanding — to put love where
  there is now hate;
To lead the race toward a juster, wiser,
  and more merciful social order, where
  each individual is evaluated in terms
  of his true worth;
To fortify the nation by the armaments
  of faith and the long range cannons
  of love;
To give guidance to those who err and
  in time redeem the environment of
  every little child;
To work for the good of all—not for the
  gain of wealth;
                and
To make an earnest trial of Jesus' Way
  of Life.[32]

The Deed, The Deed!

We know the paths wherein our feet
  should press,
Across our hearts are written Thy de-
  crees:
Yet now, O Lord, be merciful to bless
With more than these.
Grant us the will to fashion as we feel,
Grant us the strength to labor as we
  know,
Grant us the purpose, ribb'd and edged
  with steel,
To strike the blow.
Knowledge we ask not—knowledge Thou
  hast lent,
But Lord, the will—there lies our bitter
  need,
Give us to build above the deep intent.
The deed, the deed![33]

Prayers

AN OPENING PRAYER

Almighty God, unto Whom all hearts are open, all desires known, and from Whom no secrets are hid, cleanse the thoughts of our minds by the inspiration of the Holy Spirit, that we may sincerely love Thee, with pure hearts and sanctified lips worship Thee, and worthily magnify Thy holy name; through Jesus Christ our Lord. Amen.

A MORNING PRAYER

The day returns and brings us the petty round of irritating concerns and duties. Help us to play the man! Help us to perform them with laughter and kind faces. Let cheerfulness abound with industry. Give us to go blithely on our business all this day. Bring us to our resting beds weary and content and undishonored. And grant us in the end the gift of sleep. Amen.

A PRAYER FOR GUIDANCE

Direct us, O Lord, in all our doings, with Thy most gracious favor, and further us with Thy continual help; that in all our works begun, continued and ended in Thee, we may glorify Thy holy name, and finally, by Thy mercies, obtain everlasting life through Jesus Christ our Lord. Amen.

A PRAYER FOR MANKIND

O God, Creator and Preserver of all mankind, we humbly beseech Thee for all sorts and conditions of men; that Thou wouldst be pleased to make Thy ways known unto them, Thy saving health unto all nations. More especially we pray for Thy holy Church universal; that it may be so guided and governed by Thy good spirit that all who profess and call themselves Christians may be led into the way of truth, and hold the faith in unity of spirit, in the bond of peace, and in righteousness of life. Finally, we commend to Thy fatherly goodness all those who are in any way afflicted or distressed in mind, body or outward estate; that it may please Thee to comfort and relieve them according to their several necessities; give them patience under their sufferings, and bring them victoriously out of all their afflictions. And this we beg for Jesus Christ's sake. Amen.

A PRAYER FOR OUR NATION

Lord God Almighty, bless our land with honorable industry, sound learning and pure manners. Save us from violence, discord and confusion, from pride and arrogance, and from every evil way. Defend us, we beseech Thee, from the secret power and the open shame of great national sins, from all dishonesty and civic corruption; from all vainglory and selfish luxury, from all cruelty and the spirit of violence; from covetousness, impurity, and intemperance, good Lord, deliver and save us and our children and our children's children. Preserve our unity and fashion into one happy people the multitude brought hither out of many kindreds and tongues. Endue with the spirit of wisdom those whom we entrust in Thy name with authority, and may they be true servants of the people. In the time of our prosperity, temper our self-confidence with thankfulness; and in the day of trouble suffer not our trust in Thee to fail for Jesus Christ's sake. Amen.

PRAYERS

A PRAYER FOR OUR CITY

Our father's God and our God, we pray Thee for this, the city of our love and pride. We rejoice in her spacious beauty and her busy ways of commerce, in her stores and factories where hand joins hand in toil, and in her homes where heart joins heart for rest and love. Help us to make our city the common workshop of our people, where every one will find his place and task, keen to do his best with hand and mind. Bind our citizens together, not by the bond of money and profit alone, but by the glow of neighborly good will, by the thrill of common joys, and the pride of common possessions. May we always remember that our city's true wealth and greatness consist, not in the abundance of things we possess, but in the justice of her institutions and the brotherly ways of her people. All of which we ask through Jesus Christ our Lord. Amen.

A PRAYER FOR THE RURAL CHURCH

O God of our fathers and our God, we pray to Thee in behalf of the rural Church—the scattered congregations of Thy people and the thousands of Church Schools in the villages and the open country. Thou hast greatly honored and used Thy people in the rural sections in past generations. Grant, O Heavenly Father, that Thy Spirit may continue to inspire pastors and people in our rural congregations, so that a stream of living influence and spiritual power may flow from them into the life of our nation and of the world. May they be strengthened and refined amid all the discouragements of this difficult time, and may their fidelity to our Divine Master be an inspiration to all Thy people everywhere. We ask it through Jesus Christ, our Lord and Saviour. Amen.

A PRAYER FOR GOOD WILL

O Lord, who hast commanded us not to return evil for evil, but to pray for those who hate us and despitefully use us, enable us by Thy blessed example to offer a true prayer for all who may have wrought us harm. If in anything we have given offence, teach us to confess our fault, that a way of good will may be found among all classes and races and nations. Deliver them and us from hatred, malice and all uncharitableness; and may the peace of God rule in our hearts forever more. Amen.

A PRAYER FOR THE CHURCH

O God, we pray for Thy Church, which is set today amid the perplexities of a changing order, and face to face with a great new task. We remember with love the nurture she gave to our spiritual life in its infancy, the tasks she set for our growing strength, the influence of the devoted hearts she gathers, the steadfast power for good she has exerted. When we compare her with all other human institutions, we rejoice, for there is none like her. But when we judge her by the mind of her Master, we bow in contrition. O God, baptize her afresh in the life-giving spirit of Jesus! Put upon her lips the ancient gospel of her Lord. Fill her with the prophet's scorn of tyranny, and with the Christ-like tenderness for the heavy-laden and down-trodden. Bid her cease from seeking her own life, lest she lose it. Make her valiant to give up her life to humanity, that like her crucified Lord she may mount by the path of the cross to a higher glory. For Jesus' sake. Amen.[35]

A PRAYER OF DEPENDENCE

O Lord, support us all the day long of this troublous life, until the shadows lengthen, and the evening comes, and the busy world is hushed, and the fever of life is over, and our work is done. Then of Thy great mercy grant us a safe lodging, and a holy rest, and peace at the last; through Jesus Christ our Lord. Amen.

A PRAYER OF THANKSGIVING

O God, our Heavenly Father, it is in Thee we live, and move, and have our being. Every breath is a gift from Thee, and without Thy favor not one of us could draw another breath. Thou hast fed us all our life long unto this day and hast redeemed us from evil. Help us to show by our lives the song of gratitude which is in our hearts for all Thy goodness and loving-kindness toward us. We thank Thee for friends, kindred, and kindly benefactors; for the happy shelter of our homes and the inner circle of our friendships which have so enriched our lives; for health which makes hard work a joy, and even for that sickness which ripens the soul; for our fathers and mothers to whom we owe more than we can ever repay; for all gentle souls and saintly lives which have inspired us, making it easier for us to do right and harder for us to do wrong; for the happy laughter of little children which has brought us joy and peace; for all faithful toilers who, whether remembered or forgotten, have made our civilization possible; for the good counsels of faithful friends and for the voice of conscience which summons us to do Thy will, for the convictions which hold fast our faith and even for doubts which drive away what is unnecessary; for the great privilege of being co-workers together with Thee in the upbuilding of the Kingdom of God on earth; for the Church which is the mother of us all, and for Jesus Christ our Saviour who is the Master of every life, to Whom be praise forever and ever. Amen.

A PRAYER FOR OUR HOMES

O God our Father, who didst design the home to be the first Church and the first school and didst direct fathers and mothers to bring up their children in the nurture and admonition of the Lord, we thank Thee for all good homes and for what they have meant in our lives. Send down a double portion of Thy spirit upon parents and children that they may grow in grace and in the knowledge and love of our Lord Jesus Christ. May our homes be so closely linked with the Church of the living God that they may indeed be centers of righteous influence and holy purpose, the true bulwark of the nation, because in them good citizens are being made—good citizens of the Republic and good citizens of the Kingdom of God. Vouchsafe to each of us the grace to be true to our homes, useful and inspiring members of the family circle, happy to share in mutual service for one another's good. All this we ask for Jesus' sake. Amen.

A PRAYER FOR YOUTH

Our Father God, whose years know no end, before Whom the generations rise and pass away, we thank Thee for the freshness and beauty of the spring-time of life, and for the enthusiasm and radiance of youth. Do Thou in Thy mercy teach all our young men and women so to number their days that they may apply their hearts unto eternal wisdom. May all their growing powers be consecrated to high and holy ends, so that, like Jesus, they may increase in wisdom and stature and in favor with God and man. Keep them pure in heart and diligent in the work to which they have been called. And having finished their course and kept the faith, may they receive from Thee the crown of life that fadeth not away; through Him who in His youth gave His life for us upon the cross, even Jesus Christ our Redeemer. Amen.

A CHRISTMAS PRAYER

Our Father God, who didst so love the world as to send Thine only begotten Son to save us from our sins, we rejoice before Thee in the memories and inspirations of Christmas. We thank Thee for this holy day, with its gladness and melody, its wholesome conspiracies of kindness, its contagion of good cheer, its summons to give and to forgive. Help us to remember that there was "no room in the inn" for the Christ Child, that we may not share the ancient guilt, but may make ever larger room in our hearts for the Lord Jesus, who went about doing good, and who continues to lead His true followers into every ministry of helpfulness. Yea, in every service to mankind may we feel the loving heart-throbs of Him who was born a babe in Bethlehem's manger; in every agency of mercy, of sympathy, of friendship, may we feel that the heart and hands of Jesus are busy still; and may it be our high privilege to help in creating the radiant Christmas music. And so may we help to spread through all the earth the wondrous Christmas Light, especially among those little ones who are in the darkness of heartache and hunger and neglect. We ask it in Jesus' name. Amen.

A PRAYER FOR EASTER

Almighty God, our Heavenly Father, we come to thank Thee that our Lord and Saviour Jesus Christ has overcome death and the grave, and opened for us the gate of everlasting life. This is the day which the Lord hath made; let us rejoice and be glad in it. Grant that it may be for us the springtime of the soul, and that through penitence and faith we may arise to a newness of life and seek those things which are above, where Christ sitteth on the right hand of God. We ask it in the name of Him who died for us on the Cross, but who is alive forevermore. Amen.

A PRAYER OF CONFESSION

O Thou God of mercy and forgiveness, we come before Thee under a deep sense of our unworthiness and guilt, confessing that we have sinned against Thee in thought, in word, and in deed. Thou hast given us minds to know Thee, and hearts to love Thee, and wills to obey Thee; but we have broken Thy commandments and turned aside from the way of life. Yet now hear us, Father, when we call upon Thee with penitent hearts; and for the sake of Thy Son, Jesus Christ, have mercy upon us. Pardon our sins, take away our guilt, and grant us Thy peace, through Him who hath loved us and given Himself for us. Amen.

THE LORD'S PRAYER

Our Father who art in heaven, hallowed be Thy name, Thy kingdom come, Thy will be done on earth as it is in heaven. Give us this day our daily bread. And forgive us our debts as we forgive our debtors. And lead us not into temptation, but deliver us from evil; For thine is the kingdom, and the power, and the glory, forever, Amen.

Apostles' Creed, Beatitudes and Commandments

THE APOSTLES' CREED

I believe in God the Father Almighty: Maker of heaven and earth.

And in Jesus Christ, His only begotten Son, our Lord: who was conceived by the Holy Ghost, born of the Virgin Mary; suffered under Pontius Pilate, was crucified, dead, and buried; He descended into {hades; / hell; the third day He rose from the dead; He ascended into heaven, and sitteth at the right hand of God the Father Almighty; from thence He shall come to judge the quick and the dead.

I believe in the Holy Ghost: the {Holy Catholic Church / one Holy Universal Christian Church; the Communion of Saints; the Forgiveness of Sins; the Resurrection of the Body; and the Life Everlasting. Amen.

THE BEATITUDES

Blessed are the poor in spirit; for theirs is the kingdom of heaven.

Blessed are they that mourn; for they shall be comforted.

Blessed are the meek; for they shall inherit the earth.

Blessed are they that hunger and thirst after righteousness; for they shall be filled.

Blessed are the merciful; for they shall obtain mercy.

Blessed are the pure in heart; for they shall see God.

Blessed are the peacemakers; for they shall be called the children of God.

Blessed are they that are persecuted for righteousness' sake; for theirs is the kingdom of heaven.

THE TEN COMMANDMENTS

I. I am the Lord thy God, who have brought thee out of the land of Egypt, out of the house of bondage. Thou shalt have no other gods before me.

II. Thou shalt not make unto thee any graven image, or any likeness of anything that is in heaven above, or that is in the earth beneath, or that is in the water under the earth; thou shalt not bow down thyself to them, nor serve them. For I the Lord thy God am a jealous God, visiting the iniquity of the fathers upon the children unto the third and fourth generation of them that hate me, and showing mercy unto thousands of them that love me and keep my commandments.

III. Thou shalt not take the name of the Lord thy God in vain; for the Lord will not hold him guiltless that taketh His name in vain.

IV. Remember the Sabbath-day to keep it holy. Six days shalt thou labor, and do all thy work. But the seventh day is the Sabbath of the Lord thy God: in it thou shalt not do any work, thou, nor thy son, nor thy daughter, nor thy manservant, nor thy maid-servant, nor thy cattle, nor thy stranger that is within thy gates. For in six days the Lord made heaven and earth, the sea, and all that in them is, and rested the seventh day: wherefore the Lord blessed the Sabbath-day and hallowed it.

V. Honor thy father and thy mother; that thy days may be long upon the land which the Lord thy God giveth thee.

VI. Thou shalt not kill.

VII. Thou shalt not commit adultery.

VIII. Thou shalt not steal.

IX. Thou shalt not bear false witness against thy neighbor.

X. Thou shalt not covet thy neighbor's house, thou shalt not covet they neighbor's wife, nor his man-servant, nor his maid-servant, nor his ox, nor his ass, nor anything that is thy neighbor's.

Acknowledgments

Grateful acknowledgment is made to the following for the use of copyright material, quoted and adapted, in the Worship section of this book:

[1] "The Kingdom, The Power and The Glory", copyright Oxford University Press. Used by permission.

[2] Adapted from "Lyric Religion", Augustine Smith. Copyright, D. Appleton-Century Company. Used by permission.

[3] Adaptation of hymn "Our Father's God from Out Whose Hand", Whittier.

[4] Adapted from interpretation of "Christ Mourns Over the City" from Albert E. Bailey's "Gospel in Art", Pilgrim Press.

[5] "Prayers for Self and Society", James Myers, Association Press.

[6] Adapted from "The New City" by Marguerite Wilkinson, published by permission of Miss Natalie Bigelow.

[7] Adapted from a prayer by Reinhold Niebuhr, "Prayers for Services", Morgan P. Noyes.

[8] From "A Service of Recognition and Consecration", International Journal, September 1935. Copyright, The International Council of Religious Education. Used by permission.

[9] "Look to This Day", from the "Sanskrit".

[10] "The Day" by Grace Noll Crowell, from "Silver in the Sun", Harper & Brothers, publishers.

[11] "The One Thousandth Psalm", Edward Everett Hale, "Collected Works" published by Little, Brown and Company. Used by permission.

[12] "Flower in the Crannied Wall" from Collected Poems by Alfred Lord Tennyson. Used by permission of The Macmillan Company, publishers.

[13] "Earth's Crammed in Heaven", Elizabeth Browning.

[14] "The Sky-Born Music", Ralph Waldo Emerson. Used by permission of and by arrangement with the authorized publishers, Houghton Mifflin Company.

[15] "Our Christ" from "Valleys and Visions". Copyright, Mrs. H. W. Farrington. Used by permission.

[16] "Song of Christian Workingmen", Thomas Curtis Clark. Used by permission of James T. White & Company.

[17] "Jesus, the Carpenter", Charles M. Sheldon. Used by permission.

[18] "The Bible", John Greenleaf Whittier. Houghton Mifflin Company (see 14).

[19] "This Is the Church of My Dreams" by John M. Moore.

[20] "God's Temple" by Edith D. Osborne. Copyright, 1934, by Methodist Book Concern. Used by permission.

[21] "Sanctuary" by Clinton Scollard. Used by permission of Jessie Rittenhouse Scollard, Literary Executor of Clinton Scollard.

[22] "The Larger Prayer", Ednah D. Cheney. Used by permission of Lothrop, Lee & Shepard Company, publisher.

[23] "We Thank Thee Lord", John Oxenham. Used by permission Willett, Clark & Co.

[24] "Ultima Veritas", Washington Gladden. Willett, Clark & Co. (see 23).

[25] "A Boy's Prayer", William DeWitt Hyde.

[26] "A Teacher's Prayer", F. C. Rueggeberg.

[27] "In Thy Presence", Richard C. Trench. Willett, Clark & Co. (see 23).

[28] "The Lure of the Unattained", Percy R. Hayward. Copyright, The International Council of Religious Education. Used by permission.

[29] "Jesus Christ and We", reprinted by special permission of the copyrighters, Evangelical Publishers, Toronto, Canada.

[30] Excerpt from "The Vision of Sir Launfal", James Russell Lowell. Houghton Mifflin Company (see 14).

[31] "The Fatherland", James Russell Lowell. Houghton Mifflin Company (see 14).

[32] "The Tried—The Untried", Roy A. Burkhart. Copyright, The International Council of Religious Education. Used by permission.

[33] "A Prayer", John Drinkwater. Houghton Mifflin Company (see 14).

[34] "Morning Prayer", Robert Louis Stevenson.

[35] "The Church" from "Prayers of the Social Awakening" by Walter Rauschenbusch. Copyright, The Pilgrim Press. Used by permission.

The American Revised Version of the Bible used by permission of The International Council of Religious Education. Adapted to read "the Lord" instead of "Jehovah".

Bibliography of Worship Materials

ARCHITECTURE & SYMBOLISM

Beaver, R. Pierce; "The House of God"; Eden Publishing House 1935.
Vogt, Von Ogden; "Art and Religion"; Yale University Press 1929.

MUSIC

Laufer, C. W.; "The Church School Hymnal For Youth"; Westminister Press 1931.
Dickie, Mary Stevens; "Singing Pathways"; Powell & White 1929.
    (Each of these hymnals contains a section of instrumental music, simply arranged, for preludes, offertories, etc. in a church school worship)
Thomas, Edith Lovell; "Singing Worship"; Abingdon Press 1935.
    (Simplified versions of great religious music, could be used instrumentally)

POETRY

Hill, Caroline Miles; "The World's Great Religious Poetry"; Macmillan 1938.
Clark, Thomas Curtis; "The Master of Men"; Richard R. Smith 1930
Slack, Elvira; "Christ in the Poetry of Today"; Woman's Press 1928
Clark-Gillespie; "Quotable Poems," Vol. I & II; Willett, Clark & Co. 1928 & 1931.

HYMNS

Smith, H. Augustine; "The New Hymnal for American Youth"; Century Co. 1930.
Eaton, Edward D.; "The Student Hymnary"; A. S. Barnes & Co. 1937.
    (See also the three mentioned above under "Music")
Smith, H. Augustine; "Lyric Religion"; D. Appleton-Century Co. 1935.

PRAYERS

Noyes, Morgan Phelps; "Prayers for Services"; Scribner's Sons 1934.
Rauschenbusch, Walter; "Prayers for the Social Awakening"; Pilgrim Press 1925.
British Student Christian Movement; "A Book of Prayers for Students"; Richard R. Smith 1923.
Myers, James; "Prayers for Self and Society"; Association Press 1934.

SCRIPTURE & DEVOTIONAL LITERATURE

Goodspeed, E. J. and Smith, J. M. P.; "The Short Bible"; U. of Chicago Press 1933.
Page, Kirby; "Living Creatively", "Living Triumphantly", "Living Courageously";
                                     Farrar & Rinehart 1932, 1934, 1936
Pickerill, Grace G.; "Youth Adventures with God"; United Christian Missionary Society.

ART, PICTURES

Maus, Cynthia Pearl; "Christ and the Fine Arts"; Harpers 1938.
Bailey, Albert E.; "The Gospel in Art"; Pilgrim Press 1916.
Bailey, Albert E.; "Art and Character"; Abingdon Press 1938.

DRAMA

Alexander & Goslin; "Worship Through Drama"; Harpers 1930.
Whiting, Isabel K.; "Dramatic Services of Worship"; Beacon Press 1925.
Wilson, Dorothy Clarke; "Twelve Months of Drama for the Average Church"; W. H. Baker 1933.

SILENCE

Hodgkin, L. Violet; "Silent Worship"; Swarthmore Press 1919.
Hepher, C.; "The Fellowship of Silence"; Macmillan 1925.

STORIES, TALKS, TESTIMONIES

Niebuhr, Hulda; "Greatness Passing By"; Charles Scribner's Sons 1931.
Page, Kirby; (Volumes mentioned under "Devotional Literature").

GENERAL

Athearn, L. A.; "Christian Worship for American Youth"; Century Co. 1931.
International Council of Religious Education; "Journal of Religious Education"
    (203 N. Wabash Ave., Chicago, Ill.)
    (Materials for services of worship for each Sunday of the year—Primary, Junior, Intermediate, Senior and Young People's Departments).

Note: Any of the above publications may be ordered through your denominational publishing houses.